THE
HEALTHY
WHOLISTIC
DOG

ELLIOTT HARVEY, MH

D1316582

ACKNOWLEDGEMENTS

I would like to thank the following individuals for their support and assistance:

    Bruce DeBaun PHD (Animal Science)
    Carolyn Araiza DVM
    William Pollack DVM
    Pat Frederick DVM
    Linda Boggie DVM
    Lynne Friday DVM
    W. Jean Dodds DVM
    Jody Kincaid DVM
    Vickie Burton DVM
    Sarah Ober DVM
    Thomas E. Van Cise DVM
    Stephen Tobin DVM

An Open Letter to the Reader

October 1, 2000

The Healthy Wholistic Dog is a very informative book for the pet owner who is looking for answers to often-asked questions about pet health that are not readily available in most pet care books.

The writer presents clear, concise explanations about pet diseases, the various causes and preventative steps to keep your pet healthy.

After reading this book, you will want to strongly consider feeding your pet a home-cooked or raw diet fortified with herbs or nutrients to maintain or restore your pet's health.

Elliott Harvey MH is committed to providing pet lovers and owners with current information that will help alleviate unnecessary pet suffering and improve overall pet health through the use of natural remedies and natural diets.

In my 19 years of veterinary practice, it is encouraging to see more literature available to the pet owner on holistic pet care and The Healthy Wholistic Dog is one more valuable contribution to the natural pet library.

–Carolyn Araiza, D.V.M.

TABLE OF CONTENTS

INTRODUCTION

I've decided to write this book for the many animal lovers who wish to give an alternative treatment to their loving companions. Also: to veterinarians and health care practitioners who wish to expand their knowledge of natural remedies.

In todays fast paced world, convenience and low price have taken the forefront and toll on animal health. Food quality and nutritional values have been replaced by synthetics, chemicals, by-products, preservatives and road kill.

There is an alarming rise in chronic conditions that were once found in geriatric dogs. These conditions are now being observed in animals as young as 3.

Our animals are constantly being bombarded with toxins. A simple run on grass that has been chemically treated, commercial dog food with preservatives, synthetics, and low-grade ingredients cause Immune system activation. Our animals immune system is continually being called into action.

There's an alarming increase in auto immune problems such as cancer, kidney and liver failures and allergies. Is there any wonder why our animals are living sicker lives?

Animals and nature have a unique understanding of each other. When an animal gets sick in the wild they find various roots, leaves or plants to remedy conditions.

Many illness and diseases can be treated successfully with natural products. We need to rely more on quality nutrition and Mother Nature.

I would like to thank all those in the past and present involved with alternative healing.

Good Health
Enjoy

Elliott Harvey, MH

With Love to
Mom, Dad
Shadow, Travis, Buddy, Indy and Ms. Iggy

...and a special thank you to Steve Topley and Katherine Heller

CHAPTER ONE:
ALTERNATIVE THERAPIES

The acceptance of alternative therapies in recent years has been spectacular. We are seeing an abundance of people looking toward alternative medicines for their animal's health care.

What are alternative therapies? An alternative therapy is any therapy that exists outside of the mainstream. Many mainstream scientists and doctors allude to the fact that alternative therapies are unscientific, unproven and lack credibility. The ancient Romans, Indians and Egyptians all used natural remedies. The Three Wise Men delivered essential oils as a gift to the baby Jesus. The Chinese and the Indians have used alternative medicine for centuries. Today, many pharmaceutical companies are utilizing plant extracts as a source of new medicines. Recent scientific research has shown many benefits in natural medicine.

In this chapter, we will present an overview of various therapies. In submitting to any healing techniques, caution and prudence are justified. Interview the practitioner, discuss the method to be used and feel comfortable. Dogs can sense if you are nervous. Be comfortable and show confidence around your animal, and the animal will follow your lead.

ACUPUNCTURE

The Chinese healing art centers around needles being inserted into meridian lines (energy passages) to break up blockages in the natural energy flow that cause illness.

Acupuncture has been practiced for more than 2,000 years. The ancient Chinese developed this system based on the body's 12 main meridian lines. These lines flow throughout the body, incorporating all the internal organs. The Chinese believe energy flows freely through the body. When one or more of the body's internal meridian lines is blocked by disease or illness, the energy flow is disrupted.

The practitioner inserts very thin needles at various points in the body to stimulate certain areas, thereby unlocking the energy flow. Electronic stimuli passed through the needles can also be incorporated, augmenting the action. This method invokes both a physical reaction and an immune system response. Acupuncture is now considered both an alternative and a mainstream therapy.

ACUPRESSURE

Acupressure is the practice of using massage techniques along the same meridian lines as acupuncture without breaking the skin with needles. Tissue massage and manipulation techniques help unblock meridian lines. Acupressure has soft touch, medium, and deep-tissue massage, incorporating different hand and elbow techniques. Sensitivity to touch is crucial when placing pressure on the meridian lines.

AQUATIC (WATER) THERAPY

This practice utilizes various combinations of water techniques to help the healing process. Pulsating water concentrated on sore areas helps stimulate the muscle groups. An easy flow of warm water helps to relax an animal.

Pools are being utilized as a worthy source of muscle relaxation, injury rehabilitation and workouts. A swimming animal uses many muscle groups. Today, many horses and dogs utilize water therapy for ailments such as arthritis and muscle pain, as well as rehabilitation from injuries. Additional benefits include flexibility, endurance and strength conditioning.

Warm water stimulates, invigorates and then relaxes the system, and aids in relaxing striated muscles. *Cold water* helps reduce muscular swellings and pain by constricting the blood vessels, as well as aiding circulation. When alternating hot and cold water therapies, tubs are used. This technique is used to reduce swelling, improve circulation and decrease healing time.

AROMATHERAPY

Essential oils are concentrated fragrant plant extracts (a dog's sense of smell is ten times more sensitive than a human being's). Considered the life force energy of the plant, these oils contain an abundance of healing elements. It is believed that the oil travels to the part of the body in need of it. These oils deliver extremely fast therapeutic benefits. Essential oils are utilized as viral, bacteria and infection fighters, as well as for their detoxifying, anti-inflammatory, vermifuge, antiseptic and anti-spasmodic properties. They can relieve aches and pains, help with cuts and injuries, and assist in tissue stimulation and animal calming.

Essential oils can be administered by:
- Diffusion- heats the oil in an oil burner (diffuser) and allows the animal to inhale the vapors.

- Massage- gently apply a few drops of the oil (can be added to massage oil) during a massage.
- Internally- a single oil or combination of oils administered with a dropper.

Fragrances can enhance various physiological and internal changes. In the United States, aromatherapy is used in the manufacture of flea repellents, shampoos, skin products and conditioners. In Europe, essential oils are administered internally and externally to cure many afflictions.

Essential oils are very potent, but beware. Not all essential oils are the same. Many are mixed with cheap byproducts or synthetics. The unadulterated organics are superior. Make sure the label has the exact name of the plant in both English and Latin; check to see that part of the plant is distilled and for a notation stating if the product has wild-crafted plants or organic.

CHIROPRACTIC

Chiropractic therapy involves manipulation of the spinal column by hand in order to relieve various types of pain and discomfort. Practitioners seek to align the spine to maintain a balance within the systems and internal organs. The central nervous system is the focal point. A properly aligned spine allows the nervous system to transmit energy signals signifying that the body is working properly. Various conditions including, but not limited to, allergies, arthritis, circulation, colitis and disc problems have been helped using this therapy.

DARK FIELD MICROSCOPY

Live-cell microscopy allows you to see deficiencies and problems in the blood in a few minutes. A small bead of blood is placed under a high-resolution microscope. Analysis of the blood is done immediately with computerized system allowing the practitioner to get a true reflection of the problem. From this, herbal and/or nutritional programs can be developed to address the specific problems.

EXERCISE

Walking or running at various speeds with your animal promotes alertness, reduces tension, reduces fat, improves heart function, and invigorates the lungs, blood vessels and circulatory system. Movement increases oxygen intake to all parts of the body, especially in tissues. It is excellent therapy for arthritic dogs, and necessary for overweight animals.

FLOWER ESSENCES

These liquid remedies are prepared from the blossoms of wild flowers. Flower essences are prepared by a sun infusion of blossoms in a bowl of spring water that is diluted and potentized. Preservation is usually with brandy. These highly potent essences contain the specific energy pattern of the flower. Flower essences help with emotional and mental stability, resulting in improved health.

HERBOLOGY

Herbology encompasses a variety of methods utilizing the healing properties of plants, roots, leaves, flowers, bark and fungi to strengthen and heal the system. This method of healing has been around since plants first appeared on the planet. Animals have utilized plants throughout their existence.

Chinese medicinal history is said to have started over 5,000 years ago. Historians credit Chinese Emperor Shen Nong (3494 B.C.) as the father of herbal medicine. In Egypt, ancient papyrus was discovered with medicinal information. These writings date back to 1500 B.C.

Herbs have been used throughout history by various people, including the Chinese, the

Greeks, the Egyptians, the Indians (records show that Ayurveda medicine was utilized in 2500 B.C.) and others. Herbalism is an old art being revitalized today.

METHODS FOR USING HERBS INCLUDE:

- Pills. Round balls of various sizes made from herbs. They can be any size depending on the animal (usually pea sized or dime sized for larger animals). Finely grind the herbs or purchase pre-powdered herbs. Mix in either Slippery Elm or Acacia Gum (used to hold the mixture together). Slowly add spring water while mixing, making sure the mixture remains firm. Roll the mixture into pill form and place them on a plate to dry at room temperature. Once dry, brush some flax seed oil or honey on each pill for easier swallowing. Bottle and place in a refrigerator.

- Infusion. To use the volatile oil of the herb to attain the healing properties, an infusion is required. Heating the herbs will lose the volatile oil content. Mints, flowers and leaves are most commonly utilized through infusion. Combine one ounce of herb for each pint of water. Can be made like sun tea (mix in an air tight container, then place outside in the sun for up to six hours). Another method is to boil water and pour it over the herb in an air tight container, then close the container and let it stand for up to 30 minutes. An infusion can be placed in water dish, over food or given orally. It must be used within 48 hours.

- Tincture. An extremely concentrated form of the healing properties of an herb in liquid form. Healing property extraction can be accomplished with brandy, vodka, gin or glycerin. Apple cider vinegar (good against yeast and helps the skin coat) or glycerin can be used if you want to avoid alcohol. Tinctures maintain their potency for a longer duration of time than infusions, and are rapidly absorbed when given orally under the tongue. Single herbs or a blend of herbs are utilized. The alcohol content should be no less than 29 percent. Some tinctures use 50 percent alcohol and more. An 80-proof bottle contains 40 percent alcohol. The alcohol content is one half the proof number (*Note*: you can add a little water to the mixture to lower the alcohol content). Combine 8 ounces of herb to one liter of liquid (you can change amounts by adding or subtracting quantities in proportion) in a dark glass bottle. Let the bottle sit in a dark closet for 14 days. Shake the bottle twice daily. To strain, pour the liquid through a cheesecloth or muslin. The final mixture should be poured into a dark glass bottle. Dosages can vary during various stages of illness.

- Decoction. To extract the healing properties of roots, stems, bark or other herbs where the volatile oil is not needed. Use glass or stainless steel cookware only *never* use aluminum. For every 2 ounces of herb, use one pint of spring water. Bring to a boil and simmer uncovered for 30 minutes. The decoction must be used within 48 hours.

- Capsules. Oblong gelatin- or vegetable-based capsules. The size (0,00,000) determines the milligrams (amount) of herb in each capsule. Capsules contain the powered elements of the root, leaf, stem, bark or seeds of a plant. They are easier to swallow when a little ghee or oil is rubbed on the capsule. Use capsules that do not contain fillers.

- Chewables. Various shapes of compressed herbal powder with a sweetening agent or flavored for easy palatability. They are held together with cellulose (an inner tree bark fiber), acacia gum (a natural resin), carragenan (from seaweed) or slippery elm (a natural herb binder). Companies are presenting chewables as an easy-to-administer alternative to capsules. Read the label to make sure that no synthetic binders (fillers) or preservatives are used.

• Enemas. Administration of water-based herbals through the anus. Enemas help relieve constipation, remove toxins, reduces fevers, fight tumors, resist infections, rid worms (anus itch), aid in circulation, cleanse the colon by helping it absorb nutrients that ward off infections and invigorate the liver and kidneys. Acute or chronic conditions are helped by the use of enemas. Coffee enemas are utilized for constipation and toxin removal (use drip coffee; organic if possible). For large dogs, use three scoops of coffee and one quart of water, brew and let it stand until it is lukewarm. Use tinctures of Kyolic garlic, Wormwood and Black Walnut for worms (30 drops of each in a quart of warm water), and Usnea Lichen, Larix, Echinacea, Goldenseal or other herbs in tincture form (use 25 drops of each herb

in quart of warm water) for infections.
For small dogs use a bulb syringe,
for large dogs a turkey baster. Coat
the trunk of the applicator with ghee,
petroleum jelly or vegetable oil. Use a
pint of liquid for small dogs (use half
of the tincture amount) and a quart for
large dogs. Insert the applicator trunk
into the rectum and slowly squeeze half
of the mixture into the rectum. Allow the
animal to move around, and then repeat
the procedure using the remaining
liquid. For other afflictions use the
appropriate herbal tincture.

• Spray. A topical used on the surface of
the skin for various skin conditions.
Topicals are water- or aloe vera-based
and enhanced with essential oils. The
action of a quality spray is immediate.
Sprays can be used for cuts, flea
repellents, flea killers, skin ailments and
hot spots.

• Poultice. Used as quick relief for various
problems by applying crushed or
powdered herbs directly on the injury.
Typical applications include: ligament
damage, inflammations, muscular
problems, toxin elimination, infections,
cuts, wounds, burns, insect bites and
to cool irritated skin. Water or aloe

vera juice is added to the appropriate powdered herb or herbs. The mixture is placed directly on the problem area. A wrap holds the mixture in place.

HOMEOPATHY

Created by Dr. Samuel Hahnemann, this practice was something entirely different from what his colleagues were practicing. Homeopathy employs a theory completely opposite of modern medicine. He discovered the principle of "like cures like" (the law of similars). Hahnemann discovered that by matching the patient's symptom with a substance that elicits the same effect, the bodies own natural immune response will "kick out" the problem. Hahnemann found that when he diluted a ratio of one part substance to nine parts dilution medium, the effect of the remedy was still present. Thus he built up his potencies by dilution and succession. This led to another discovery, namely, the more he diluted and succused, the more enhanced the activity of the remedy became. The more potentized the ingredient, the stronger it becomes.

Potency dilutions are one part substance (mother tincture) to nine parts dilution liquid = X potency. One part substance (mother tincture) to 99 parts dilution liquid = C potency.

Each dilution is shaken 100 times. Further dilutions decrease the original substance, in turn increasing the potency. Dilutions of the original substance deliver a magnetic code that carries the signatures of the initial substance.

- *Low Potencies.* Mother tincture to 6C or 7C (6X –7X) acts on tissues and cells of organs. Can be repeated frequently.

- *Medium Potencies.* 12C to 30C (12X to 30X). Acts on the blood, body fluids and endocrine system. One to two times daily up to 14 days.

- *High Potencies.* 100C and up. Acts on a deeper level. Not to be repeated often. An accurate diagnosis by a qualified homeopath is needed first.

MAGNETS

Equal applications of positive and negative gravitational pull keep the system in harmony. When a force becomes greater than its counterpart an imbalance occurs, leading to illness. All creatures' bodies are made of bioelectric magnetic fields. Bi-polar magnets allow an increase in blood flow and circulation, nutrients and oxygen to augment tissue healing. The elimination of pain and waste products can be attributed to shortened healing time.

MASSAGE

This therapy involves the manipulation of soft tissues and muscles with single- or two-hand techniques utilizing various degrees of pressure and speed.

The benefits of massage include:
- Removal of toxins
- Relaxation of muscles
- Warming of muscles prior to use
- Reduces tension
- Stimulates circulation
- Reduces sweating
- Increases range of motion
- Helps ease muscle spasms
- Nice touching experience

(*Note*: All techniques must be performed moving from the head toward the back of the animal. This front-to-back movement allows the toxins to be moved away from the heart toward the elimination organs. If done in reverse, the toxins will be pushed toward the heart and brain.)

THE VARIOUS TECHNIQUES OF MASSAGE INCLUDE:
- Effleurage aids in the movement of venal blood and other interstitial fluids to the

heart, kidneys and liver. The greatest effect is on the circulatory system. Effleurage helps drain the tissues of wastes and toxic substances such as lactic acid (a major cause of muscle soreness). Vasomotor centers are stimulated to dilate the small blood vessels of the skin which increases peripheral circulation and creates heat at the coat surface. The technique also aids the lymphatic system.

• Kneading impacts on muscles, underlying bones, and the blood vessels that supply these vessels.

• Passive Touch helps calm the animal with a sedative effect. The technique is non-threatening and brings warmth to coat. Lay the entire hand on animal, when coat starts to feel warm, move the hand to a different location.

• Skin Rolling helps drain waste from the coat, increase glandular action for better coat and helps with dermatological problems. Use small, quick strokes with the palm and fingertips moving from the back of the head to the tail.

• Fulling increases circulation, aids in healing, stimulates the coat and increases nutrients to area.

- Compression increases blood flow to muscles, warming them.

- Chucking involves using the thumb and fingertips to grab the skin in a sort of pinching motion. The speed of chucking moves from slow to medium to fast. It helps to relax tight muscles and stretch contracted muscles.

- Thumb Gliding uses the thumb to glide down the rib cage from the top of the back to the end of the rib cage in medium to light fashion. This removes wastes, breaks down scar tissue, reduces pain, relaxes stress points and increases circulation as the muscle tissue relieves itself of waste products.

- Digital Kneading increases flexibility, helps remove toxins and increases nutrients into tissue muscle.

- Jostling encourages increased blood flow and lymph flow to the tissues being worked. The muscle temperature rises, allowing greater flexibility and a larger range of motion.

- Percussion stimulates the senses and perks up nervous system. Mentally arousing, it warms the surface and

17

aids in the relaxation of muscles. This includes tapping, hacking, cupping, strapping and brushing.

- Stretching helps maintain flexibility, improves flexibility, bridges the gap between inactivity and vigorous exercise by preparing the muscles, tendons and ligaments for activity, raises body and deep muscle temperatures, provides improved flexibility for performances and injuries prevention and aids in injury rehabilitation.

- Stroking provides a calming and quieting effect, slows the blood flow to specific body parts, slows the heart rate, reduces pain, and helps relieve congestion and inflammation.

- Cross Fiber Techniques help the lymph system remove toxins, increase flexibility and transport nutrient-rich oxygenated blood.

- Angel Wing increases blood flow to flat muscles such as shoulders, triceps and deltoids.

- Raking increases blood flow. This technique is used on round surfaces

such as the anterior shoulder, the pectorals, the gluteals and the hamstrings.
• "V" Spread involves all cross-fiber areas.

MICRONUTRITION CELLETECH SUPPLEMENTS

Micronutrition celletech supplements involve using "data cards" that carry the unique signatures of the substance instead of the homeopathic bioactive compounds (the magnetic code) of the herb. Magneto Geometric Application equipment uses an interpreter, an amplifier containing a permanent magnet to create the magnetic code of the substance. This allows for the highest potencies to be created in a succinct period of time.

MUSIC THERAPY

Music has long been utilized for behavioral modification. Various soothing music such as mellow sea sounds, soft rippling forest sounds and various classical music symphonies have a calming and tranquilizing effect.

GEMMOTHERAPY / PHYTOTHERAPY

This approach utilizes the nucleus of the young plant buds, shoots or immature plant tissues to attract the highest concentration of vitamins, amino acids, plant hormones, minerals and active constituents in the plant. Cultivating the young plant allows the extract to have dynamic properties not available in the adult plant. The remedies are organ and illness specific. The plants specific organ properties have been referred to as "the stem cells of plants". This therapy is essential to regain health on the cellular level. The elimination of toxins and metabolic waste products is paramount with gemmotherapy in essence the therapy helps wash away accumulated cell poisons.

The plant medicine is extracted via alcohol and glycerin to strength of 1/10 solution, which corresponds to Hahnemanns' first decimal. This strength provides maximum benefits on a consistent basis.

UTILIZATIONS:

Allergies	Black Currant, Beech, Rosemary, Juniper
Eczema	Black Currant, Cedar of Lebanon, Elm, Walnut Tree
Mass Infected Eczema	Black Walnut

Psoriasis	Rye, Cedar of Lebanon
Pancreatitis	Walnut Tree, Black Currant
Adrenal Glands	Alder, Birch
Kidneys	Ash Tree, Juniper, Birch
Arthritis/Rheumatism	Mountain Pine, Grape Vine, Dog Rose, Blackberry, Virgin Vine
Anti-inflammatory	Black Currant
Anxiety	Linden Tree
Immune Booster	Birch
Periodontis	Birch, Oak
Liver	Rosemary, Olive Tree, Juniper
Pancreas	Walnut Tree
Colic	Cowberry
Anemia	Tamarisk, Hazelnut Tree
Thyroid	Hounds Tree (hyperthyroid)

Gemmotherapy uses fresh buds and young shoots, roots, rootlets and catkins of trees to make concentrated extracts. They are freshly picked and macerated for 21 days to ensure maximum vitality and effectiveness.

Gemmotherapy belongs to the realm of Phytotherapy but differs since it only uses the buds and/or young shoots of the plants. The embryonic part of the plant is particularly effective for drainage, which means detoxifying actions on the body.

Gemmobase (5% or 10/1) - Buds and young shoots are organically grown, freshly picked and harvested in the spring and macerated in water, vegetable glycerin and alcohol for 21 days then filtered. The mother maceration is 5% (10/1) concentration. This process is heavily concentrated and utilizes less alcohol with a greater amount of nutrients.

Chapter Two:
Food: What Are You Buying?

In today's fast-paced environment, convenience and price have overshadowed nutrition. Buying food products is not a major campaign for many individuals. Pricing and purchasing convenience have overtaken the importance of nutrition. Manufacturers spend millions of dollars on advertising, colorization of packages, visual appeal, special savings, smell, palatability and more in order to entice you to purchase their product. With all the money that has been spent on presentation, the product has to be inexpensive to be profitable.

Ingredients

Many veterinarians and natural practitioners are coming together over the issue of better quality ingredients in animal food. There has been an alarming increase in allergies, diabetes, arthritis, skin problems, visual problems, hyperactivity, organ and gland problems and cancer.

Our animals are getting overloaded with toxins. Environmental toxins in the air and water are compromising animals internal systems, as well as by chemicals and pesticides. Animals systems can not clean out toxins as rapidly as they are accumulating. Add nutritionally deprived food, preservatives, synthetics, antibiotics, and our pets' health deteriorates further.

Many problems can be alleviated with high quality food. It is amazing how an animals system can benefit when you change diet to quality food and add nutritional support. My neighbor used to buy the cheapest pet food available. He had a beautiful rottweiler (aka The Licker). Poor nutrition and improper breeding conditions resulted in severe bone deformities in his and many other dogs. His second dog, a mutt and a big lover, gained an enormous amount of weight and became very lethargic. His skin became taught, he was balding and he developed thyroid problems.

When ingesting food made from inferior ingredients, the animal's internal organs and immune system are working overtime. Something has to give and too often it is the animals health. Is it any wonder there are so many sick animals?

Bill Pollack, DVM states, "The massive majority of animal illnesses would go away if the animal is not fed commercial pet food."

Have you ever read on a pet food label the actual amount of digestible ingredients in the product? Labels state the "<u>Minimum</u> Daily Requirements." Are you to feed the same amount to an active dog as a lazy dog?

Additionally, the palatability of a product is critical. Some dogs cannot stop eating those delicious morsels. The result? Serious Health Problems for the animal. How can a dog stay healthy? We have notied 52 lb bag of dog food for $12.99. What do you think is in these inexpensive foods?

LABELS: WHAT ARE YOU BUYING?

ALLERGENS

Allergens include beef, tuna, milk products, turkey, yeast, corn, pork, eggs, wheat and fish. The grade, or quality, of the substance and the amount used in the product can cause allergies (*Note*: Many brands use an extruded process where foods are cooked and steamed and pressed at high temperatures causing substantial nutrient loss).

COMMERCIAL GRADE (AKA MYSTERY PELLETS)

CEREAL MILL RUN

Utilizes cereal fines (sifted off particles) that may contain excessive amounts of sugar and sweepings from the floor that may include unknown materials. Not fit for human consumption.

POTATOES

A recent newspaper article stated potatoes have a known cancer-causing agent. *Acrylamide* is a natural occurring carcinogen formed solely when potatoes are cooked or heat processed. The vast majority of dog and cat foods utilize cooked potatoes as an inexpensive source of starch. Evidence of this problem was addressed in 1986. This can be another reason for health problems and the upswing of cancer in pets...

GROUND CORN

Ground whole kernels, usually #2 grade. May cause allergic reactions depending upon both the percentage used in product and the corn's origin.

CORN GLUTEN MEAL

Leftover remnants from a processed run of corn oil or corn syrup. Nutritionally, corn gluten meal is inferior. Used as filler, it is not easily digestible. Allergic reactions may result depending on the amount used in the product.

WHEAT BRAN

Allergenic. Floor sweepings may be incorporated into by-product.

SOY

Soy may cause allergic reactions, intestinal gas and bloating. Used to boost protein, it has inhibitors that block the uptake of certain nutrients. It is difficult to digest.

BEET PULP

Dried residue of sugar beet. Has no nutritional value except as a stool firmer and possibly as a nutritional food source for Probiotics. Used as a sweetener for palatability.

CORNCOBS, CORNHUSKS, PEANUT SHELLS

A very inexpensive source of fiber, nutritionally inferior

MILL RUN

Produced from a variety of ingredients, including floor scrapings, leftovers from processed run and unknown amounts of foreign matter.

MEAT BY-PRODUCTS

Meat by-products involve the use of *any portion of the animal available during processing,* including hooves, hide, horn, hair, organs, entrails, blood and bone. The animal may vary from batch to batch. By-products may have toxins, hormones (bovine growth-BGH), steroids, cancer or antibiotics. They are unfit for human consumption.

Rendering is part of the "4Ds": Dead, Diseased, Dying and Disabled. The term encompasses companion animals, road-killed animals, farm animals or any other animals used for pet food. Not allowed for human consumption, rendered material is mixed together and reprocessed for animal food. This is a very inexpensive food source.

TURKEY

Turkey may cause some allergic reactions. It is an excellent protein source, and provides a good supply of vitamins and minerals including iron, zinc and selenium.

POULTRY BY-PRODUCT MEAL

Can be from any form of poultry. Produced from ground-up feet, heads, beaks, feathers, hair and organs, it may also include animal tissue. It may include salmonella, cancer or antibiotics. Unfit for human consumption.

BEEF AND BONE MEAL

Produced from grinding up parts of beef or pork producing animals. Preservative enhanced, it may contain various toxins including drugs, heavy metals, steroids and pesticides. Human grade bone meal is a good source for calcium and magnesium. The proper ratio is 1.75 parts calcium to one part phosphorus to 1/2 part magnesium to calcium.

BLOOD MEAL
Dehydrated blood used for protein source.

FISH MEAL
Produced from the dehydrated ground tissue of fish. Heads, glands and tails may contain heavy metals.

FISH OFFAL
Produced from leftovers, fish offal contains no meat. Created by grinding up guts, scales, skin, head and eyeballs. It contains low amounts of protein and holds no nutritional value.

LIVER
Usually comes from an unknown source and is unfit for human consumption. It may contain flukes.

Chemicals and Preservatives

BHA / BHT PRESERVATIVES
Chemicals known to be cancer causing used for long shelf life.

RED DYE # 40 / SODIUM NITRATE (COLORING)
Items used to make food look more palatable. Possible link to cancer.

ETHOXYQUIN

Preservative, may not be on label. Considered to be a major cause of disease, infertility and skin problems.

FLAVORINGS

Various items are incorporated into dog food for palatability, including reprocessed animal parts, beef tallow, pork fat, poultry fat and discarded, chemically reprocessed restaurant grease fat.

Semi-moist foods are loaded with chemicals, dyes, sugars, propylene glycol (which causes problems with digestive tract, inhibits nutrient uptake) and additives. Semi-moist foods enjoy a long shelf life, but are nutritionally inferior.

A major "veterinarian" office brand lists their first ingredients as follows:
- Ground Corn
- Poultry-by-Product Meal
- Corn Gluten Meal
- Dried Beet Pulp

In addition, BHA, propyl gallate, BHT and ethoxyquin are incorporated.

Another of their products, according to the label, contains the following: Ground Corn, Soybean Mill Run, Poultry-By-Products Meal,

Ground Peanut Hulls, Natural Flavor and Iodized Salt, as well as BHA and BHT.

This is a major, well-known brand! Read the labels; your animal's health is at stake.

GENERIC BRANDS

Generally of poor quality and deficient in needed nutrients. Dogs are consuming massive amounts of chemicals each year, resulting in toxic overload. Your pets' systems are not capable of continually fighting this needless stress.

Why is there a great difference in pricing between the foods?

Bill Pollack, DVM states that "Human food created the pet food industry. Waste products needed a new avenue of sale: animal food. Manufacturing plants cut up and utilize all the best and nutritious parts of an animal for human consumption. The scraps or garbage are processed for dog food. It is nutritionally dead."

OTHER INGREDIENTS INCLUDE:

- Ocean Fish. Deep water or ocean fish contain high amounts of Omega 3 and 6 Fatty acids, good for the arteries. Also a source of vitamins A, B3, and K. The fish utilized *are not the typical fish* found in the human food industry. These are usually waste fish and may contain heavy metals.

- Turkey and Chicken- high in vitamins, minerals and provide an excellent protein source.

- Oatmeal helps lower cholesterol. An excellent source of carbohydrates and fiber. Contains B vitamins, minerals and vitamin E.

- Whole Dried Egg is a source for protein, linoleic acid, calcium and phosphorus.

- Lecithin: A source for antioxidants, choline, phosphoric acid and essential fatty acids. Helps metabolize fats and aids in digestion.

- Barley provides a good source of vitamins and minerals.

- Alfalfa provides a complete and balanced nutrition source. It contains all known vitamins, chlorophyll, calcium, magnesium, phosphorus, potassium and balanced minerals. Helps neutralize the intestinal tract.

- Carrots, Apples are a good source of antioxidants, vitamins A, C and K, iron, folic acid and calcium.

- Kelp is high in iodine (thyroid function) and converts carotene to vitamin A. A source for B vitamins, minerals and trace elements. An organ cleanser as well as a stimulator for hair skin and nails.

- Garlic is a detoxifier, a natural blood purifier, an antibiotic and anti-parasitic.

- Blueberries reduce blood sugar and contain anti-diarrhea properties.

- Desiccated Liver Organic builds red blood cells and aids with liver disorders. Provides vitamins A, D and C, B-Complex, calcium, copper, phosphorus and iron.

- Spinach is a cleanser, stimulating the liver functions, gall bladder and colon, and helps circulation. Contains chlorophyll, vitamins A, B, CoQ10, calcium, iron, potassium, sodium and trace elements.

- Flax Seed is rich in Omega 3 fatty acid, helps to fight heart disease, and is a good source of fiber, protein, phytonutrients and carbohydrates. Strengthens bones, nails and teeth and helps with healthy skin.

- Linoleic Acid (omega 6) is an essential fatty acid for healthy skin and coat.

- Ground Sunflower Seeds are a source of Omega 6, as well as essential lipids and protein.

- Lactobacillus Acidophilus is a friendly bacterium needed in the colon to reduce cholesterol levels and aid in digestion, as well as helping absorb nutrients more efficiently.

- White Rice is said to be easily digestible and is unlikely to cause allergic reactions.

- Brown Rice is nutritious and contains many B-vitamins, calcium, phosphorus, and iron. It is said to be easily digestible.

- Rice Bran is a good source of soluble and insoluble fiber and micro trace minerals.

- Taurine is an amino acid that supports the central nervous system and muscle tissue.

- L-Lysine is an amino acid for growth, enzyme production, fighting viral infection, gland regulation and the assisting of the assimilation of enzymes.

- Glucosamine Hydrochloride boasts anti-inflammatory and pain relieving properties. It aids injured joints.

- Chondroitan Sulfate works synergistically with Glucosamine, aiding in new cartilage formation.

- d-Alpha-Tocopheryl Acetate is the actual structure of vitamin E and is an anti-oxidant.

CANNED FOODS

Canned foods may contain up to 79 percent water. Canning and cooking involve temperatures in excess of 300 degrees. It is nutritionally inferior. Enhanced with synthetic nutrients.

*A learned operations director of a large pet food manufacturer with 35 years in the business relayed to me that all vitamins, enzymes and amino acids are in the extruded kibble even though the heating process reaches temperatures in excess of 300 degrees. *However; their chemical structure (characteristics) has been altered by the cooking process, the nutritional value is negated.*

NATURAL FOODS

WHAT IS NATURAL FOOD?

Natural foods are foods that do not contain chemical additives, food or flavor additives, corn syrup (sugars), by- products or chemical preservatives.

One of the large pet manufacturers that utilize corn and peanuts had a recall for contamination of vomitoxin and mycotoxin.

- Check to see if your animal is digesting rice. Examine the stool for undigested rice. Rice and worms look very similar.

- With a pre-made diet, one hour prior to feeding give the animal a good digestive enzyme complex (enzymes Pro+ is excellent). Add one or two capsules of essential fatty acid complex, or one or two teaspoons of organic flax seed oil or wild salmon oil to the food.

HUMAN GRADE RAW FOOD

Many pet owners are changing to a more natural feeding process, the raw food prepared diet (BARF). Raw foods offer the best source of raw protein, nutrients, antioxidants and enzymes for an animal. Human-grade organic is the best. It contains No steroids, pesticides, or antibiotics are involved.

- Steves offerings are complete and balanced, exceeding the guidelines of the FDA, the USDA and the AAFCO. The chicken, beef and turkey (plus vegetables) are properly prepared for maximum nutritional benefit. Both freeze-dried and frozen versions are available.

- Halshan sports an FDA-approved label on the package. It offers 12 various diets with buffalo, duck breast, venison, ostrich, lamb, and muscle meats. Coleman beef, chicken, and turkey are antibiotic-and hormone-free. The company also offers organ meat (sold separately) and vegetables.

- Primal utilizes organic fruits and vegetables. Beef and chicken come from family owned farms in Northern California. They are utilizing a second plant in S. Cal.

- Pat McKay products are produced
  and labeled for human consumption
  as federally inspected by the USDA.
  Utilizing "organic" vitamins and
  minerals, all products are fresh frozen.
  Offerings include beef, chicken,
  lamb and turkey with or without 12
  vegetables. Four additional varieties,
  including chicken liver, beef heart,
  lamb kidney and fish, come with 12
  vegetables.

- Sojourner Farms offers premixed
  packages of grains, herbs and nuts. The
  meat source is added to the mix.

- Natures Variety Product varieties include
  Lamb, Chicken, Turkey and Beef.
  Released Organic Chicken product.

- Jeffrey's Natural Foods in San Francisco
  is a new concept in food stores.
  They make your raw food diet on the
  premises.

- Northwest Naturals offers various flavors

THE BEST OF BOTH WORLDS
GREAT LIFE DOG FOOD – GREAT LIFE PERFORMANCE PET PRODUCTS

FDA and USDA approved facility. Wholistic based kibble with added organic fruits and vegetables layered after cooking with a raw food diet including pre-probiotics, green vegetables, sprouts, green tripe, coral calcium, 74 trace minerals encased in salmon oil.

Full Active Nutrition. Utilizes Organics and Free Range Sources. No Corn, Hormones, Steroids, (Meals), Soy, White Rice, By-Products, Potatoes or Allergenic Ingredients.

No Refrigeration Required. Chicken, Beef, Lamb and Buffalo.

Great Life Dog Food (Rubicon Series) /Rx Formulas – Grain and Potato Free Formula. Utilizing Tapioca and Jicama as starch sources. Raw food based kibble encased with organic coconut and wild salmon oil. Excellent nutrient profiles. Superior food in all respects.

DEHYDRATED FOOD

The Honest Kitchen; add warm water to rehydrate mixture. One cup makes a pound

HOMEMADE DIETS

Many holistic veterinarians prefer a good home-cooked meal for animals. Discussions are ongoing as to whether or not a raw meat diet is healthier. Some individuals believe that, through years of breeding, dogs have lost their desire and/or need for raw meats.

I don't believe this to be the case. Many qualified practitioners have stated that the catalyst of life (enzymes) is missing from

39

prepared packaged foods and home-cooked foods. A common problem with home-cooked meals is overcooking. Vitamins, enzymes and other nutrients can be cooked out of the food. Prepare a good essential fatty acid mix supplement and a good supplement to replace the lost nutrients.

To date there has been no problem feeding a good raw diet. I've been told of salmonella poisoning from an individual who purchased meat for her family and dog at a local market. Both human and animal became ill. This woman and I had a discussion regarding a raw meat diet. She explained that her bitch kept developing skin problems, and she wants to switch her to a raw meat diet. However, she decided it is too expensive and time consuming to make. It was then that I noticed a bag of inexpensive dog food in the back of her new Toyota Land Cruiser.

RAW DIET PREPARATION

To clean raw meat or vegetables; use grapefruit seed extract or 3% hydrogen peroxide or OxyDoc in a bowl of spring water and let it sit for two to three minutes. Fresh young broccoli sprouts are very nutritious.

Before starting a raw diet, a detoxification regimen needs to be administered. Gradual reduction of commercial food with added enzymes and probiotics are required. Slowly add the raw food into the meal. The animals overall condition and health needs to be taken into account, along with the animal's age. This will help coordinate the time frame into a complete raw food program.

THIS IS A PROTEIN/GRAIN FORMULA:
- 70% Protein. Raw turkey or chicken (with finely ground necks twice a week), beef, lamb, venison or buffalo. Organic preferably, with no hormones or pesticides Use organ meat twice a week.
- 25% Fresh Vegetables. They should be raw, chopped or lightly steamed, including dark green leafy vegetables, string beans, zucchini, broccoli, carrots, watercress, dandelion, bok choy, summer squash, sweet potato and amaki.
- 5% Grains. Sources include oatmeal, buckwheat, spelt, kamut, millet, amaranth, couscous and rye.

Rotate your protein sources. Additional ingredients can include one or two tablespoons of organic flax seed oil, salmon oil, yogurt (1 teaspoon to 1-2 tablespoons, 2 to 4 times a week), 1-2 organic raw brown or green eggs a week (grind into powder), 1 tablespoon of barley juice powder, or kelp.

Vicki Burtin, DVM states, "All dogs are not the same. A working sled dog needs a different mix than a couch potato. Raw foods provide essential nutrients. Individual health needs must be paid attention to. Know your animal's needs."

CHAPTER THREE:
VITAMINS

Vitamins are essential for an animal's proper growth, reproduction and overall health. All living creatures need vitamins. Animals utilize vitamins to regulate chemical reactions within the body. These chemical reactions institute the process that form tissues and produce energy. Vitamins and minerals work in an animal's body to help maintain good health.

Vitamins are classified in two groups, *water-soluble* and *fat-soluble*. Water-soluble vitamins consist of the B-Vitamins, C, bioflavonoids, choline and inositol. They are easy to assimilate and start working as soon as the digestive system absorbs them. They are carried by the circulatory system to specific tissues. These vitamins are not stored in the body like fat-soluble vitamins are, so signs of deficiency manifest quicker in the animal.

Fat-soluble vitamins (A, E, D and K) need proper fat assimilation to work. The intestines absorb these vitamins, while the lymphatic system carries them to various parts of the body. These vitamins are stored in the liver, reproductive organs and tissues. Fat-soluble vitamins assist in the synthesis of enzymes and maintaining sound cell-membrane structure. Since these vitamins are stored in the body, deficiencies take longer to materialize.

Fat-soluble vitamins stay in the liver, tissues and reproductive organs for a longer period of time than water-soluble vitamins. An animal's body cannot produce the daily vitamin requirement.

(*Note*: Vitamins A, E, C and B1 can be destroyed by food processing, light, heat, various storage conditions including long shelf time, and excessive moisture. Chelated forms of vitamins are preferred as they are specifically buffered to avoid upsetting the stomach.)

WATER-SOLUBLE VITAMINS

BIOTIN

- Insufficiency: Dermatitis, high blood cholesterol, appetite loss and bad skin and hair.

- Actions: Metabolizes protein, fats and carbohydrates. Cell growth, utilization of B-vitamins, healthy sweat glands and nerve tissue.

- Sources: Meat, brewers yeast, poultry, saltwater fish, whole grains, licorice.

CHOLINE
- Actions: Metabolization of fat and cholesterol along with Inositol, as well as absorption and fat utilization. Nerves.

- Sources: Lecithin, whole grains, organ meats,

FOLIC ACID
- Insufficiency: Anemia, immune system weakness and nerve problems.

- Actions: Protein metabolism, controls depression and anxiety. Proper formation of red blood cells and promotes healthy cell division. Antioxidant.

- Sources: Barley, beef, lamb, chicken, whole wheat, desiccated liver, brewer's yeast, brown rice, wheat germ and whole grains.

PABA
- Actions: Protein metabolism, skin protector. Affects intestinal bacteria's ability to produce folic acid. Helps in the development of red blood cells.

- Sources: Desiccated liver, whole grains, burdock, corn silk and horsetail.

LECITHIN
- Actions: Main source of choline, structural component of cell membranes. Helps prevent cardiovascular and arteriosclerosis disease.

- Sources: Brewers yeast, grains, fish, wheat germ, aloe vera, bee pollen, fenugreek.

B-VITAMINS

Insufficiencies can lead to nerve problems, growth, intestinal problems, poor nutrition and absorption, convulsions, dull hair, dry skin and gastric trouble. They deal with the proper absorption of food and normalize functions of nervous system and brain. The B-vitamin group is essential for proper health of skin, hair, eyes, mouth and liver.

B-1 (THIAMIN)
- Insufficiency: Energy loss, nerve, brain and heart trouble. Gastrointestinal problems. Leg weakness, edema, weight loss, liver and heart difficulties.

- Actions: Needed for muscle tone, metabolism of carbohydrates. Converts fatty acids into steroid hormones as cortisone, progesterone. Healthy skin. Builds energy and appetite, digestive aid, aids heart and liver function.

- Sources: Rice bran, wheat germ, rice polish, peanuts, green leafy vegetables, brown rice, poultry, brewers yeast, kelp, dulse, spirulina, alfalfa, burdock, comfrey, hops, nettle, barley juice powder, fenugreek, jujube, peach kernal (tao-ren) and garlic.

B-2 (RIBOFLAVIN)
- Insufficiency: Lack of energy, dermatitis, retarded growth, eye problems, digestive disorders, nervousness and anemia.

- Actions: Formation of antibodies and red blood cells, fat and protein metabolism. Antioxidant. Thyroid hormone metabolism and tissue repair.

- Sources: Wheat germ, wild rice, meat, poultry, dulse, fenugreek and green leafy vegetables.

B-3 (NIACIN)
- Insufficiency: Nervous disorders, gastrointestinal problems and dermatitis.

47

- Actions: Healthy skin, metabolism, circulation, lowers serum cholesterol and digestion aid. Adrenal gland aid. Increases synthesis of B-vitamins and helps intestinal flora.
- Sources: Desiccated liver, brewers yeast, carrots, wheat germ, whole wheat, rice bran and fenugreek.

B-5 (PANTOTHENIC)

- Insufficiency: Stress, immune system weakness, osteo- and rheumatoid arthritis. Food allergies, faulty digestion

- Actions: Metabolism of fat, protein and carbohydrate production. Lower blood cholesterol levels. Diabetes. Synthesis of hormones. Inflammation. Maintains a healthy adrenal gland.

- Sources: Beef, brewers yeast and fresh vegetables.

B-6 (PYRIDOXINE)

- Insufficiency: Depression, skin problems, (seborrheic dermatitis), anemia, arthritis and mouth inflammation.

- Actions: Healthy blood cell production and blood vessels, nervousness, formation of blood antibodies. Carbohydrate, fat and protein metabolism. Sodium-potassium balance and immune function.

- Sources: Brewers yeast, carrots, green vegetables, meat, wheat germ, cantaloupe, cabbage, potatoes, dulse, rice bran, alfalfa and oat straw.

B-12 (COBALAMIN)

- Insufficiency: Nerves, anemia, digestive distress, weight loss and weakness.

- Actions: Healthy bone marrow, red blood cell production, metabolization of fats and carbohydrates. Helps nerves.

- Sources: Brewers yeast, desiccated liver, mackerel, sea vegetables, kelp, alfalfa, angelica, barley juice powder, eyebright, spirulina and white oak bark.

VITAMIN C

Insufficiency can lead to fragile gums and joints and poor nutrition and overall poor health. Low energy, uneven heart action, improper digestion, eye problems, slows wound healing, and weakened immune system. Diabetes. Weakened bone and cartilage.

- Actions: Cancer prevention, antioxidant. Strengthens blood vessels, works as a cardiovascular helper. Strengthens immune activity. Reduces serum cholesterol levels. Aids in tissue growth and repair, the formation of collagen and the conversion of folic acid into active form. Improves the availability of selenium and enhances adrenal gland function and the healing of wounds.

- Sources: Animals produce vitamin C in the liver. Green vegetables, black currants, kale, dulse, parsley, alfalfa, amaranth, barberry, bee pollen, blue vervain, burdock, celery, chickweed, chicory, comfrey, echinacea, euryale, elder, garlic, ginger, golden seal, hawthorn berries, juniper, nettle, purslane, parsley, plantain, queen of the meadow, rose hips, red clover, schizandra, scullcap, MACA MACA, spirulina, watercress, wormwood, yarrow and yellow dock, LicAmA.

FAT-SOLUBLE VITAMINS

VITAMIN A
- Insufficiency: Loss of weight, loss of energy, slow growth, impaired glandular activity, infections, poor vision, improper digestion, diarrhea, poor skin conditions, poor bone and tooth development.

- Actions: An antioxidant, it enhances immunity and increases infection resistance, as well as promoting growth and reproduction.

- Sources: hot pepper, dandelion, dock, carrots, fish liver oils, desiccated liver, garlic, broccoli, sweet potatoes, tomatoes, collards, peaches, watermelon, spirulina, dulse, cantaloupe, burdock, borage, fennel, alfalfa, mullein, red clover, parsley, lemongrass, astragali, plantain, hops, horsetail, eyebright, uva ursi, sage, birch, chicory, comfrey, couch grass, echinacea and elder.

VITAMIN D

- Insufficiency: Brittle bones, poor body tone, respiratory infections, bad teeth, constipation and nervousness.

- Actions: Required for calcium and phosphorus absorption. Mineral metabolism, steady heart and nerve action. Immunity. Helps guard against arthritis and in the absorption of vitamin C.

- Sources: fish liver oils, sunlight, saltwater fish, eggs, alfalfa, horsetail, nettle, parsley, bee pollen, Irish moss, sarsaparilla, and watercress.

VITAMIN E

- Insufficiency: Sterility, vitality, muscular weakness, deficiency red blood cells (anemia). Nerve destruction, kidney disease, and cancer.
- Actions: Reproduction. Antioxidant, lactation, healing of wounds. Protects red blood cells. Cancer prevention, protects against toxins, increases "good" HDLs to help lower cholesterol levels. Reduces insulin for diabetes. Utilization of fatty acids. Protects against cardiovascular disease.

- Sources: Cold-pressed vegetable oils, brown rice, barley, wheat germ, rice germ, dulse, desiccated liver, kelp, organ meats, alfalfa, dandelion, flaxseed, angelica, bee pollen, birch, burdock, echinacea, shavegrass, licorice, scullcap, slippery elm, spirulina and yarrow.

VITAMIN F

- Insufficiency: Impaired growth, skin disorders, eczema, nervousness and diarrhea.

- Sources: Liquid vegetable oil, whole grains, eggs, spinach. Polygala.

VITAMIN K

- Actions: Blood clotting, bone formation and density.

- Sources: Green vegetables, blackstrap molasses, oatmeal, safflower oil, liver, wheat, agrimony, alfalfa, chicory, green tea, corn silk, Irish moss, kelp, nettle, safflower, slippery elm.

ANTIOXIDANTS

A free radical is an electron that has been left unpaired with another electron and which bonds with an atom or group of atoms. Unpaired electrons cause instability in the system, leading to free radicals. Free radicals can cause cell damage which lead to a degraded immune system. With the immune system below optimum performance levels free radicals can scavenge the system causing infections, diseases, cancer, and degenerative problems. Antioxidants are used to defend against free radicals.

CO-Q-10

- Insufficiency: fatigue, periodontal (antioxidant) disease and diabetes.

- Actions: Superior antioxidant. Affects the respiratory system (asthma, allergies).

- Sources: Mackerel, beef, peanuts and spinach.

ROYAL JELLY

Royal jelly is called "The food of the queen bee" maintains normal body functions, strengthens the immune system to protect against infections and disease. Increases endurance and energy. Royal jelly has antibacterial and anti-viral properties. It also hastens the formation of bone tissue and speeds up the healing of wounds Royal Jelly contains fatty acids, protein, carbohydrate, lipids, all vitamins, minerals, hormones, sterols, 17 amino acids, RNA and DNA. Royal Jelly is an extremely healthy and beneficial antioxidant.

GINGKO BILOBA

Helps brain function and circulation with improved blood flow. It stops free radicals from destroying cells and aids hearing, energy aid and supports healthy blood, as well as oxygenating all parts of the body.

GRAPE SEED EXTRACT

A free radical scavenger, grape seed extract helps the elasticity of capillaries, preventing heart problems. Considered to be more powerful than vitamins E and C.

GREEN TEA EXTRACT

Neutralizes free radicals, protects against various cancers and helps lower serum cholesterol levels.

KRILL OIL

Significant amounts of Phospholipids, powerful antioxidants, omega oils 3(epa & dha) 6.9, choline, and Vitamins A, E, astaxanthan and sodium.

ALPHA-LIPOIC ACID:

Certain fats are needed for proper health functioning. Alpha-Lipoic acid is an essential fatty acid in the Omega 3 family. Alpha-Lipoic acid neutralizes free radicals in fatty and watery regions of cells and improves the effectiveness of other antioxidants. It extends the lifespan of Vitamin C, CO-Q-10 and glutathione, and helps renew vitamin E. It is used to help combat cancer, diabetes, circulatory disorders, heart rhythm abnormalities and hormonal imbalances. Alpha-Lipoic acid is able to break the blood/brain barrier to help repair brain tissues.

(*Note*: Fish oils, including cod liver, salmon, and mackerel, as well as flax seed oil and menhaden, are good sources of Omega

MINERALS

Minerals are found throughout the world as naturally occurring elements. Vitamins cannot be utilized without minerals. Minerals are the chemical reactor for many biological functions, including the acid / alkaline balance, cardiovascular system function, nerve function, chemical reactions, hormone production, digestion and fluid balance, as well as for energy, tissue growth, assimilation of nutrients in foods, reproduction, bone and skeletal development, muscle response and the delivery of messages through the nervous system.

Chelated minerals are preferred. Chelated minerals are bound by amino acids, which increase absorption and are easier on stomach walls.

CALCIUM

- Insufficiency: Improper digestion, brittle bones, poor bone growth, nervousness, anemia, stomach acidity, asthma, hay fever, blood disorders, tooth decay, malnutrition, goiters, wrinkled skin, nervousness eczema, elevated blood cholesterol levels and inflammations.

- Actions: Enzyme activity, blood clotting, nerve impulses. Aids digestion and the utilization of Vitamins A, C and D,

phosphorus and magnesium. Helps
absorb B12 and aids in the proper
utilization of iron.

- Sources: Dulse, kelp, green leafy
  vegetables, brewers yeast, cabbage,
  oats, oyster shell, watercress, yogurt,
  alfalfa, aloe vera, barley juice powder,
  burdock, chamomile, chickweed,
  chicory, comfrey, cuttlefish, dandelion,
  dragon bone, fennel, fenugreek,
  flaxseed, ginger, golden seal, hops,
  hydrangea, mullein, nettle, oat straw,
  parsley, plantain, red clover, rose hips,
  spirulina.

PHOSPHORUS
- Insufficiency: Affects intelligence. Can
  lead to loss of bone mass and calcium.
  Extreme hunger alternating with lack of
  appetite. Weakness.

- Action: Energy metabolism, replication
  of cells, proper pH in body. Utilization of
  fats, carbohydrates and proteins.

- Sources: Brewers yeast, garlic, meat,
  poultry and green leafy vegetables.

MAGNESIUM
- Insufficiency: Nervousness, acid buildup,
  digestive disorders, stiff muscles, soft

bones, aggressiveness, epileptic seizures and diabetes.

- Actions: Promotes muscle strength and tone. Cardiovascular, energy regulation and metabolism, enzyme activity. Calcium and potassium uptake, cholesterol reduction and cancer prevention.

- Sources: Kelp, potato, green vegetables, apples, dulse, garlic, brewers yeast, wheat, alfalfa, aloe vera, barley juice powder, comfrey, schizandra, hydrangea, chamomile, fennel, mullein, parsley and red clover.

ZINC

- Insufficiency: Growth, immune resistance, impaired taste and smell, impaired vision and skin problems.

- Actions: Boosts immune system, cell repair and growth. Protects against environmental toxins.

- Sources: Brewers yeast, dulse, kelp, lamb, poultry, whole grains, alfalfa, burdock, bilberry, chamomile, comfrey, golden seal, marshmallow, Oregon grape, scullcap, slippery elm and valerian.

IRON

- Insufficiency: Anemia, obesity as well as affecting intelligence. Reduced white blood cell counts and mouth inflammation.

- Actions: Transportation of oxygen to body parts, oxygenation of red blood cells. Enzyme activity for energy and the immune system. Production of hemoglobin and myoglobin.

- Sources: Desiccated liver, meat, poultry, green leafy vegetables, whole grains, brewers yeast, dulse, kelp, rice bran, wheat bran, blackstrap molasses, agrimony, alfalfa, aloe vera, barley juice powder, echinacea, fenugreek, mullein, milk thistle, nettle, parsley, red clover, slippery elm and pau d'arco.

COPPER

- Insufficiency: Anemia, bone defects, nerve problems, pigmentation, hair, cardiovascular problems and raised serum cholesterol levels,

- Actions: Formation of elastin, collagen, bone development. Antioxidant, immune system, taste and energy production.

- Sources: Barley, blackstrap molasses, oats, green leafy vegetables, chickweed, comfrey, echinacea, golden seal and red clove.

MANGANESE

- Insufficiency: Glandular disorders, weak tissue, defective reproduction functions.

- Actions: Enzyme metabolism including fat, carbohydrates and blood sugar metabolism. Growth and repair of bones and connective tissue. Proper functioning of nerves. Bacteria fighter, free radical scavenger. Immune system. Strengthens liver, kidneys, pancreas, lymph, heart and brain.

- Sources: Parsley, carrots, blueberries, green leafy vegetables, alfalfa, burdock, barberry, blessed thistle, gentian, horsetail, Oregon grape, yellow dock, yucca

CHROMIUM

- Insufficiency: Glucose intolerance, stunted growth.

- Actions: Reduction of body fat. Cholesterol levels.

- Sources: Brewers yeast, brown rice, calf liver, chicken, corn, dulse, potatoes and stevia.

SELENIUM

- Insufficiency: Muscular weakness, growth problems, fertility, heart disease.

- Actions: Antioxidant, cancer prevention. Skin helper, arthritis.

- Sources: Brewers yeast, chicken, garlic, kelp, dulse, wheat germ, organic vegetables, whole grains, and organ meats.

IODINE

- Insufficiency: Hardening of arteries, goiter.

- Actions: Proper functioning of Thyroid.

- Sources: Kelp, garlic, dulse and summer squash.

POTASSIUM

- Insufficiency: Malnutrition, diarrhea, vomiting, kidney damage, dry   skin, constipation, elevated cholesterol levels and thirst.

- Actions: Cardiovascular helper, balance of fluids in cells. Nerve helper, water balance (sodium) and blood pressure.

- Sources: Poultry, vegetables, brown rice, garlic, brewers yeast, potatoes, winter squash, wheat bran, yam, alfalfa, aloe vera, cascara sagrada, celery, jicAmA, chamomile, hops, chaparral, comfrey, echinacea, evening primrose, fennel, nettle, plantain, spirulina and yucca.

CHAPTER FOUR:
EAR PROBLEMS

Initial recognition of the early signs of an ear problem can significantly reduce anxiety, discomfort and distress. Observing your dog's behavior and responding quickly can avoid serious problems and permanent damage. And be sure to remember that flop-eared dogs are notorious for ear problems.

I recently brought Max, a four-year-old golden retriever mix, home from the local pet shelter. I gave Max to my wife when she came home from work. She was excited and very happy. I hadn't been informed, however, that Max is a thief! He'll steal socks, kids' shoes, he even tried to steal a wheel from a baby carriage our neighbors were putting together.

My wife took Max to our local veterinarian for his free examination. The previous owner had listed no health problem conditions. Unfortunately, Max had *a severe ear and skin problem.* The veterinarian was polite, explained to my wife about the ear problem and gave Max shots and antibiotics. The first part of the "free" exam was $170.

Nine days later, the problem returned. After another $107, the veterinarian informed my wife Max would need to be on steroids the rest of his life. That was when she finally asked me to help Max.

First, I cleaned his ears with solution #1. I then gradually changed his diet to raw food, adding enzymes, a tablespoon of salmon oil, along with some fresh carrots, and squash, as well as changes his eating regiment to two meals a day.

Max has never gone back to the veterinarian. His ears are healthy, he's happy, his fur is glowing and he's still stealing things.

Symptoms of Ear Problems
- Inflammation
- Offensive odor
- Scratching (one or both ears)
- Swelling (one or both ear flaps
- Sensitivity to touch
- Head tilting
- Head shaking (with or without scratching)
- Discharge from the ear

Ear problems can be caused by such factors as:
- Allergies (from food, impaired immune system, inhalation)
- Yeast Infection (strong odor, sticky, dark brown wax)

- Liver or kidney problem (both ears affected)
- Stress
- Mites (contagious. Cause intense itching, dark brown discharge. Part of the arachnid family). Can cause secondary infections.
- Bacterial (fight injury, may have some pus) or
- Fungal (antibiotic reaction, water in ear)
- Inner or middle ear infection (head tilted to one side, uncoordinated, falling)
- Crusting at edge of ears (fly bites)
- Thyroid
- Ticks will latch onto the ear canal. They are supported by the host's blood. The can cause secondary infections when initial signs are left untreated.
- Foxtail plant (matter sticks in ear)

NUTRITIONAL SUPPORT

Many ear problems can be alleviated with a change to a natural, preservative- and allergen-free diet. Also, consider switching from municipal water to purer natural spring water.

HERBOLOGY

Detoxify the system with an internal cleanse. Choose from Power (Ejuva),

Envirozoan (Bio-Energetics) or Detoxaid (BioSpec). A good combination is aloe vera, black walnut hulls, grapefruit seed extract, papaya leaf, and senna.

Administer 1-2 tablespoons of yogurt every other day as well as a daily enzyme supplement and zinc.

EAR INFECTIONS
HERE ARE SOME ALTERNATIVES FOR CLEANING AND HEALING PROBLEMS:

- OxyDoc. Add one teaspoon of OxyDoc to 8 ounces of water. Wash the ear with the solution.

- Combine one part Aloe Vera Juice, 2 parts Apple Cider Vinegar and 5 drops Colloidal Silver (500ppm). Administer ear with solution, and then massage the ear canal for one minute (a squishing sound will be heard). Let animal shake its head, and then clean out the ear with a soft tissue. Repeat every 2-3 days.

ALTERNATE COMBINATIONS:
- Boric Acid.
- Isopropyl alcohol, boric acid and violet leaves
- Clean ear with a solution of Green Tea and Maitake.

- A combination of Yeast Buster and Aloe Vera Juice. Open 1 Yeast Buster capsule and add 2 oz of Aloe Vera Juice (preservative free, organic) mix together. Put a small amount in ear 2x a day to start followed after 3 days by alternating days and one time daily. DMSO is helpful.

MITES

Combine neem oil (8 drops), 1/2 oz. olive oil, 6 drops of golden seal tincture, 6 drops of echinacea tincture and one capsule of vitamin E. Mix together and pour into a small bottle. Put one dropper into the ear, then massage. Clean the ear after the dog stops shaking its head. Repeat twice daily every other day, for 10 days. After three days, repeat the procedure if needed.

TICKS

Remove the entire body and head with tweezers. Heating up the tweezers may help to loosen the tick's hold. Some individuals use "Tombstone" flea spray and heat.

FOXTAIL PLANT

Combine olive oil and vitamin E, apply to the ear, and then clean out the foxtail.

HOMEOPATHY

- *Hepar Sulph: 30c, 100c* Pain, displeasure with being touched, inflammation, liquid in ear,
- *Tulasi: MT, 30c* Discharge from the ear, offensive pus from ear, hot ear
- *Elaps Corallinus: 30c* Intolerable itching, greenish discharge.
- *Pulsatilla: 6c* Hearing problems, thick discharges, and offensive odor, swollen and red.
- *Aconite: 15c* Sensitive, hot, red, swollen.
- *Merc.15c, 30c* Yellow discharge, offensive odor, bloody.
- *Chamomile: 15c, 30c* Searing pain, swelling, frantic reaction to touch, calming effect
- *Rhus Tox: 12x* Chronic infection
- *Kali Birch: 30c* Hematomas (blood vesicle)

USING ESSENTIAL OILS AGAINST TICKS

Administer a few drops of the solution below on the tick; the ticks should fall off the animal. Once they are off, use a hot match on the ticks.

The solution:
- 50% Terebinth
- 20% Olive Oil
- 15% Lavender
- 10% Lemon
- 15% Turmeric

(*Note*: The dosages provided in this book are intended for large, active animals. Before beginning any supplement program, consult your natural health practitioner or qualified animal health specialist.

Chapter Five:
Arthritis

Arthritis is an inflammation of the joints associated with a metabolic deficiency. Arthritis is not a local problem but a system problem. When the body's organs are not functioning correctly due to nutritional deficiencies, metabolism suffers. Improper metabolization leads to an accumulation of minerals and calcium in the joints. Pain increases as the cartilage becomes brittle and dry, and ligaments lose their flexibility and tone. Faulty nutrition, an improper diet, vitamin or mineral deficiencies, stress, toxins, environmental factors, genetics or infection can cause arthritis.

Hip dysplasia in larger dogs is a relatively common problem. A buildup of excessive calcium in the hip sockets combined with inflammation causes dysplasia. Poor nutrition from when the dog is a puppy leads to the soft tissue growing at a disproportionate rate to the muscular skeleton. This leads to a hip socket improperly formed or incorrectly bonding with the ball of the thighbone.

Many cases of arthritis and hip dysplasia can be prevented. Pregnant bitches need a calcium-rich diet with good amounts of nutritionally beneficial vegetables, vitamins and minerals, including trace minerals. Commercial pet food should be avoided. A good raw food diet or a superior natural product is needed. Extra calcium, magnesium, phosphorus, silicon, vitamins A, B, and C, alfalfa, carrots, ground eggshells, kelp, and essential fatty acids should be included.

SUPPLEMENTS

Supplement	Dosage
Vitamin A	7500iu
B-3	75 mg
B-6	15 mg
Vitamin C + Bioflavonoids	3500mg daily
Enzymes	Per Label
Collagen Type II	1 gram
CMO	20mg
Vitamin E	400iu
Calcium Chelate	750mg
Magnesium	375mg
Copper	1 mg
B 12	100mcg
Folic Acid	100mcg

Wild Salmon Oil	1-2 teaspoons
Organic Honey	1 teaspoon
Pantothenic Acid	125mg
Boron	1mg
Kelp	1 teaspoon
Essential Fatty Acids	Per label
Zinc	15mg
Grape Seed Extract	30mg
CoQ 10	30mg
Aloe Vera Juice	1 tablespoon daily

It is easy to obtain supplements; however, the body has a difficult time transporting most commercial minerals from the digestive tract to the blood. Above sea level, coral calcium seems to be the most easily transportable, providing the maximum health benefits. Naturally ionized (1000 times smaller than colloidal minerals) with 74 balanced trace minerals, coral calcium is almost totally absorbed and utilized.

This organic mineral compound, along with enzymes, probiotics and proper nutrition, may help alleviate bone problems.

HERBS

I received a frantic call from a woman named Sonja living in a little town in

California. Her pet was stricken with a severe case of arthritis. Walking was almost impossible. Her vet put her on a variety of medications, all to no avail. She visited a local pet store. The owner advised her to try the formula below.

After using the product, her dog is active again, happy, off all medications and loving life. The pet store closed, so Sonja became frantic that she wouldn't be able to acquire the product. She was directed to another source, and now she and her dog are taking walks together again.

This chewable formula is excellent and is available from Doctors Finest Pet Products:

- Sea Chondroitan - contains calcium, phosphorus, protein (manufactures hormones, antibodies, enzymes, Chondroitan sulfate (a vital compound in connective tissue, healthy joints, cartilage building), MPS (lubricates joints).

- Green Mussel - contains SOD (anti-inflammatory, MPS (soundness of joints, skin & bones).

- Turmeric- Anti-inflammatory, antioxidant.

- Devils Claw- Anti-rheumatic, blood cleanser. Eliminates uric acid deposits in joints.

- Horsetail (Shavegrass)- Increases calcium absorption. Promotes healing of bones & connective tissue.

- Yucca- Blood purifier, Anti-inflammatory. Vitamins A, C, B-complex, calcium, potassium, phosphorus, manganese, copper.

- Dandelion- Beneficial for liver, kidneys, gallbladder, stomach, pancreas, intestines and blood. Nutritive.

- Celery Seed- Neutralizes uric and other acids. Vitamins A, C, B-Complex, calcium, potassium, iron, phosphorus.

- Magnolia Bark- Anti-inflammatory, relaxes striated muscles.

- Magnesium- Assists in potassium and calcium uptake. Prevents calcification of soft tissue. Fights acid buildup. Neutralizes toxins.

- Chamomile- Calmative, digestive aid, anti-inflammatory.

- Yellow Dock- Tones entire system, blood purifier, good for the liver, gallbladder, spleen and colon.

- Ginger- Stimulates circulation, antioxidant, reduces spasms.

ADDITIONAL BENEFICIAL HERBS

- Pau D'Arco: eliminates toxins, purifies blood.

- Comfrey: cleanses system

- Yarrow: blood cleanser

- Chaparral: eliminates uric acid

- Lobelia: relaxant, removes obstructions from body

- Burdock: blood cleanser

- Turmeric: antioxidant, anti-inflammatory.

- Clematis: antibacterial, anti-fungal, relieves pain,

- Coral Bean Bark: relaxes striated muscles, anti-fungal, kills parasites.

- Gentian: stimulates pituitary gland, alleviates pain, reduces arthritic problem.

- Wild Pepper: relaxes tendons, strengthens tendons and muscles.

- Orient Vine: relieves painful swelling in limbs and joints.

- Tayuya: blood purifier, aids digestion.

- Quebra Pedra: a diuretic, it stimulates elimination of uric acid.

- Yerba Mansa: a diuretic, it excretes nitrogenous acids, anti-inflammatory, antibacterial, anti-fungal

- Chuchuhuasi: potent anti-inflammatory, muscle relaxant, anti-rheumatic, immunostimulant.

- Carqueja: Anti-inflammatory, anti-rheumatic, digestive aid, tonic.

- Cordia: Antiarthritic, anti-inflammatory, tonic.

- Iporuru: Antibacterial, anti-inflammatory, antimicrobial, anti-arthritic.

- Scarlet Bush: antirheumatic, antifungal, anti-inflammatory, immunostimulant, diuretic.

ARTHRITIC FORMULAS:

- Pumpkin Py w/ joint mobility herbs- organic based cookie- Great Life Performance Pet Products

- ArthroAid: Doctors Finest Pet Products. Eliminator and maintenance.

- Liquid Health: Mixture of various joint helper ingredients in a liquid base.

- Syn-Flex: Similar idea as above.

- Power Walk: Liquid with many different outstanding nutrients, excellent results.

ESSENTIAL OILS: EXTERNAL RUB
Take one oz. flax seed oil or canola oil. Mix in 5 drops rosemary, 4 drops lavender, 4 drops birch, 2 drops peppermint and 2 drops ginger.

HOMEOPATHIC

- *Nat. Fluor: 15c* Hard to move. Awkward movement.

- *Cal Phos: 6c* Stiffness and pain,
  Weakness in extremities, joint swelling.

- *Apis Mel: 6c* Swelling of various parts,
  joints sensitive to touch.

- *Acidum Lac: 6c* Pain in joints

- *Dulcamara: 6x* Exposure to damp, cold
  air, muscle tightening, and pain in
  limbs. Diarrhea, acute skin eruptions.

- *Arnica: 6x* Very painful in all joints while
  moving. Back and limb pain, uneasiness
  while walking.

- *Rhus Tox: 12x* Painful swelling of joints,
  greatly debilitating. Better when moving,
  worse in damp cold weather.

- *Formica Rufa: 6x* Stiff, contracted joints.

- *Calc Fluor: 15c* Cracking sound in joints,
  cysts, and tumors.

- *Causticum: 15c* Painful walking,
  unsteady walk, feet itch, stiff knees, stiff
  tendons.

GEMMOTHERAPY
- Mountain Vine
- Grape Vine

- Dog Rose
- Black Currant
- Wild Woodvine
- Birch
- Blackberry
- Virgin Vine

CHAPTER 6
CANCER

Cancer is a disease of the body's cells. The loss of ability to grow healthy cells that divide and replenish themselves by abnormal growth and random order causes tumors. It is unnerving to realize that 25% of dogs will have some form of cancer in their lifetime, and an even-higher ratio (50%) of older dogs will succumb to cancer.

There are various trains of thought as to what may cause cancer. Viruses, vaccinations, nutritionally inferior foods, pollutants, electro-magnetic fields, radon, fluoride, cigarette smoke, chemically enhanced and processed pet foods, engine exhausts (especially diesel), flea and tick collars, overuse of x-rays, ozone damage, insecticides, asbestos, industrial pollutants and pesticides are some of the culprits thought responsible for the disease.

VARIOUS CANCERS AND THEIR DEFINITIONS

- *Leukemia.* Rapid reproduction of white blood cells in blood forming organs: bone marrow, spleen, and lymph nodes, malignant.

- *Malignant Tumors.* Travel destroying tissues and organs through out the system.

- *Benign.* Not spreading

- *Adenocarcinoma.* Glandular tissue involvement, malignant.

- *Lymphomas.* Cancer within the lymph system, malignant.

- *Lipomas.* Fatty deposit tumors, benign.

- *Osteosarcomas.* Cancer of the bone, malignant.

- *Melanoma.* Pigmented skin cells, malignant.

- *Hemangiosarcomas.* Cancer of spleen, malignant.

- *Carcinoma.* Tumor of the skin, may affect any organ, spread via blood stream, malignant.

WARNING SIGNS

- Abnormal swellings that continue to grow

- Skin or mouth ulcerations, sores that don't heal
- Bleeding from mouth, nose, urinary tract, vagina, rectum
- Eating or swallowing problem or indigestion
- Breathing problems
- Changes in bowel or bladder tendencies
- Malignant growths
- Hesitation to exercise - loss of energy
- Lameness or stiffness of movement
- Appetite loss-weight loss
- Offensive odor
- Testicle abnormality
- Nagging cough or vocal problems
- Chronic constipation with anal swelling

Nutrition

Home Cooked Meals or Raw Food Diets ONLY

System Detoxer	Envirozoan (Bio-Energetics), Power (Ejuva)
Pro Vitamin A	7500iu to 15,000iu (American Biologics)
B-Complex	100mg
Ester C- Complex with Bioflavonoids	5000 +mg daily (to bowel tolerance),
Super Multiple	Eclectic, Miller
Green SuperFood Complex (1 1/2x label)	Crystal Star
Selenium	50mg
B-17	per instructions
Glandular extracts	American Biologics
eNZYmes Pro+	Great Life Performance Pet Products
CoQ 10	90mg daily
Oxygen Supplement	Homozoan
Shark Cartilage per instructions	American Biologics, Doctors Finest Pet Products
Raw Cabbage	
Organic Green Tea Extract	2-6 capsules daily
Organic Apricot Kernel	1-7 per day

HERBS

CANCER TEA 1

2 parts Graviola, 1 part Cats Claw, 1 part Astragalus, 1 part Burdock, 1 part Violet Leaves, 1 part Chaparral, 1 part Red Clover, 1 part Ho-Shou-Wu (Fo-Ti), 1/2 part Sheep Sorrel, 1/2 part Curcumin, 1/4 part Yellow Dock, 1/4 part Boldo. Bring to a boil in spring water, cool. Add 3 parts Agaricus Blazei Murril, 2 parts Maitake*, 2 parts Reishi, 2 parts Cordyceps. Flavor with honey or stevia.

CANCER TEA 2

1 part Graviola, 1 part Red Clover, 1 part Echinacea (aug. root), 1 part Cats Claw, 1 part Burdock, 1 part Green Tea, 1/4 part Senna, 1/4 part Sheep Sorrel, 1/4 part Milk Thistle. Bring to boil in spring water, cool. Add: 3 parts Agaricus Blazei Murril, 3 parts Turkey Tail, 2 parts Reishi, 2 parts Maitake*, 1 part Cordyceps. Flavor with stevia or honey.

(*Note:* The above herbal formulas can be purchased pre-mixed directly from the author complete with cooking instructions.)

* Maitake D has been shown to increase red blood cells.

Herbal Cancer Broth and Meal

1 Organic Chicken, Amaranth or Barley or Brown Rice (cook per directions). Add spring water, and then cover chicken. Cook until done. Remove from heat, remove chicken and add to hot broth 5 grams Agaricus Blazei, 4 grams Maitake, 2 grams Reishi, 2 grams, Turkey Tail and 5 grams Corydyceps. Add 1-cup organic unpeeled carrots and 1 teaspoon Kyolic garlic. Simmer for two minutes. Place amaranth or barley in bowl, and then add portions of chicken meat. Cover with broth. Add parsley, kale and young broccoli sprouts.

- Add Larex 2-3 times daily to all protocols.
- Mushrooms are organic mycelium.

Immune Deficiency Formula, Doctors Finest Pet Products

Cangoway Formula, Great Life Performance Pet Products

Additional Beneficial Herbs
- Anamu
- Dragons Blood
- Shrimp Flower
- Pau d'Arco
- Espinheira Santa
- Trifala

- Guacatonga
- Perriwinkle
- Mayapple

As well as...

- Graviola- this rainforest herb is regarded as a very potent cancer fighter.

- Una De Gato (Uncaria Tomentosa)- Considered one of the most important botanicals in the rainforest. This herb is a powerful cellular reconstitutor. It is used for gastritis, ulcers, cancer, rheumatism and arthritis. Research shows that this powerful herb activates the immune system by increasing lymphocytic (white blood cell) activity.

- Astragalus (Astragalus Mongolicus) - Considered a superior herb in China. It is one of the most important tonic herbs. The vasodilation effect of this herb improves blood circulation, enhances nutrition, strengthens digestion and the immune system and promotes both antibacterial and diuretic action.

- Yew Tips (Taxus Baccata) - A superb source of natural laetrile. Laetrile has been proven an effective anti-cancer agent.

- Violet (Viola Odorata) - This herb is used to soften hard lumps and counteract cancer. The properties in violet seem to be able to reach places only the blood and lymphatic fluids penetrate.

- Red Clover (Trifolium Pratense) - An excellent blood purifier, as well as a good dietary supplement (vitamins A, C, F and P, B-complex vitamins, high mineral content, selenium (an antioxidant), cobalt, nickel, calcium, copper, sodium and manganese). Soothing to the nerves and a powerful anti-cancer aid.

- Yellow Dock (Rumex Crispus) - An astringent and blood purifier. It is one of the best blood builders available. It will tone up the entire system, stimulate bile elimination and nourish the spleen and liver.

- Mandrake (Podophyllum Peltatum) - An extremely strong glandular stimulant. Very effective against mercurial poisoning, lymphatic problems, and obstructions of the liver and gallbladder.

- Burdock (Arctium Lappa) - This is one of the premier blood purifiers in the herb kingdom. Helps to rapidly clear the blood of harmful acids and impurities. Burdock contains a lot of vitamin A, P and B-complex, and consists of 12% protein and 70% carbohydrates.

• Chaparral (Larrea Divaricata) - A strong antioxidant, anti-tumor agent, painkiller and antiseptic. Chaparral is one of nature's best antibiotics. It is good for bacterial, viral and parasitic infections. The major constituent of chaparral is a substance called NDGA. NDGA has been shown to have anti-cancer properties.

(Note: All herbs and mushrooms need to be pesticide, insecticide and radiation free! Organic are preferable.)

SALVE

For external tumors add in equal amounts the following; Violet Leaves, Red Clover, Echinacea, Cats Claw, Aquaricus, Burdock, Radix Asparagi, Chaparral and Yew Tips. Use 1/2 amount Myrrh, 1/4 amount Poke, Suma. Place in an ovenproof glass pot and cover herbs with first-pressed virgin organic olive oil. Bake at 200F for 2 1/2 hours,
Strain mixture through a cheesecloth, then add one Vitamin E capsule and 1-2 oz.

Beeswax. Place on the stove at low heat.

Mix the ingredients together until the beeswax is completely melted. DO NOT BOIL. Pour the contents into a container and let it solidify. Pre-made salve is also available via Doctors Finest Pet Products.

EXTERNAL OINTMENT

One quart organic with no preservatives: Aloe vera gel, 1/2 oz of each of the following, in fine powder form: Fo-Ti, Red Clover, Echinacea (aug. root), Chaparral, Burdock, Astragalus, Usnea Lichen, Pau D'Arco, Suma, Yerba Mate and Yew Tips. Add 1/8 oz. Poke, also in powder form, and 4 tablespoons Sea Minerals and 25 drops Liquid Oxygen.

Mix until a thick paste consistency is achieved. Apply to the affected area.

HOMEOPATHIC

Lynne Friday, DVM utilizes the pathological tissue from the sick animal. She sends it to a Celletech lab where a sarcode is formulated. A sarcode activates the immune system and helps to wall off the tumor.
The success rate is as high as 90% in cases dealing with lipoma.

- *Chemo 6c* helps create an immune response to the chemotherapy drugs in advance of administration. The body is not overwhelmed by the new toxic agent (chemotherapy). Enhances chemotherapy effect with minimum side effects.

- *Carsinosin nosode* concerns constipation, respiratory problems, skin problems.

- *Scirrhinum 30c* affects tumors, cysts, and hardening of glands.

- *Carbo Animalis 3x, 30c* concerns weakness, swelling of glands and pains.

- *Argentricum Nit 30c* deals with fear, digestive problems and fatigue

- *Chelidonium 15c* concerns liver problems.

- *Custom Nosode* involves homeotherapeutics.

OXYGEN THERAPY

Take your animal into the forest or someplace that is surrounded by trees and away from the pollution. A walk along the ocean is also beneficial. If walking is a problem, drive to the site, park and just enjoy nature.

ELLIOTT HARVEY, MH

CHAPTER SEVEN:
ALLERGIES

The immune system of animals and people is the body's self-contained healing element. The response by the immune system from contact with allergens (dust mites, molds, pollen, dander, environmental pollution, foods, feathers, flea bites and insect stings) and skin contact with chemical irritants (flea collars, insecticides, various detergents, and petroleum-derived products) leads to a release of histamine, serotonin and leukotrienes

In dogs, the degree of sensitivity is proportionate to the release of these compounds. Many breeds have inherent tendencies to specific allergies (atopy).

SYMPTOMS MAY INCLUDE
- Sneezing
- Watery eyes
- Itching, scratching
- Paw licking and chewing
- Underarm scratching
- Vomiting and diarrhea

Dogs' systems are extremely sensitive to many of the common elements found in today's environment, including chemicals, air pollution, water pollution, petroleum products, food, and grooming aids.

An ever-increasing number of animals are developing allergies. Food sensitivity is a major area of concern. Paying attention to labels and understanding what you're giving your pet is very important. Pets are sensitive to items as pork, by-products, wheat, corn, turkey, beef, milk, yeast, eggs, dyes, chemical preservatives and flavoring. A good natural diet is beneficial in reducing allergies. An immune system in good order fights off harsh allergenic reactions.

A dog with a severe allergy may go into anaphylactic shock. Signs include vomiting, diarrhea, prostration, respiration difficulties, poor coordination and pale mucous membranes. Anaphylactic shock appears quickly, and is life threatening to the animal.

NUTRITION

First and foremost in combating allergies is a changing of the animal's diet to a quality pet food, a homemade diet or a raw food diet.

- Oxygen with colloidal silver Earths Bounty, American Biologics
- Whole body cleanse American Biologics

- A selection of apricots, peaches, plums, nectarines, grapefruit pectin and honey (using two months prior to pollen season also helps with diarrhea)
- A lot of spring water

Keeping the systems flowing (defecating 2-3 times daily) helps the removal of toxins. A strong immune system is of paramount importance. Cleanse the system with a combination of aloe vera, papaya leaf, black walnut hulls and red clover. Mix and shape into pills, then coat them with honey.

NUTRIENTS

Vitamin C and bioflavonoids	2500mg (to bowel tolerance)
Vitamin A	up to 15000 iu
Zinc Gluconate	15mg
B-Complex	up to 100mg
Enzymes/Probiotics	eNYZmes Pro+
Extra B12 and B6	
Pantothenic Acid	30mg
Vitamin E	200iu
Bio Acidophilus	American Biologics
CO-Q-10	up to 90mg
Gingko Biloba	up to 80mg
Grape Seed Extract	100mg
Essential fatty acids	1-2 teaspoons daily

HERBS

Blood cleansing and nutritional herbs are utilized for allergies. To create a liquid extract, combine: 1 part yellow dock, 1 part Echinacea, 1 part Oregon grape, 1 part dandelion, 1 part burdock and 1 part red clover with 1 part turmeric, 1 part larex, 1/8 part licorice and 1/8 part ginger (if it is being made into a tea, add honey or stevia to sweeten).

Use up to 10 drops of the extract in the animal's water, three times a day.

• Nettles w/Larex and Vitamin C	Freeze-dried concentrate; Eclectic
• Alfalfa	Freeze-dried organic
• Envirozoan	Bio-Energetics

Additionally, Reishi mushroom; Amor Seco and Guaco have antihistamine properties.

HOMEOPATHY

- *Aconite 6c, 30c* used for anaphylactic shock

- *Ambrosia 15c* for watery eyes, sneezing, itching and diarrhea

- *Rhus Tox 15c* for red and swollen eyes, sneezing and itching

- *Spongia Tosta 15c* for watery eyes and dripping nose

- *Sulphur 15c, 30c* for skin rashes and dermatitis

- *Apis Mel 15c* for swelling, redness and hot skin

- *Ars Alb 15c* for raw skin on the ears, itching pain and offensive odors from the ear

- *Urtica Urens 15c* for eruptions, itching, blotches and burning

- *Wyethia 15c* for itchy palate and dry mucous membranes

Histamine 30c from Nosode,Boiron and Celletech. An allergy kit is available from Celletech.

ENZYME SUPPLEMENTATION

In his clinical practice, Jim Smith, VMD has noticed a significant reduction in food allergies with enzyme supplementation. He is a proponent of enzyme therapy for many ailments.

All enzymes are not alike. Fungal enzymes grown on mushrooms, for example, are tolerant to various pH changes in the system. Purity, concentration and broad pH tolerance is critical to the enzyme's effectiveness.

GEMMOTHERAPY
- Black Currant
- Beech
- Rosemary
- Juniper
- Birch

Chapter Eight:
Diabetes

Diabetes mellitus results from the pancreas being unable to produce enough insulin for the body to utilize blood glucose correctly. The body needs insulin to convert sugar from foods eaten into energy for all cells in the body.

Diabetic ketoacidosis is life-threatening complication if mellitus is untreated or poorly treated.

Diabetes may be attributed to the following

- Drugs
- Commercial foods
- Chemicals
- Incorrect nutrition
- Inferior breeding practices
- Preservatives
- Obesity
- Pancreatitis
- Auto-immune disorder
- Viral infection

The pancreas is one of the most important organs for digestion. Failure to treat Diabetes can result in problems with the kidneys, eyes, liver, cardiovascular system, motion, nerves and in infections.

Signs of Diabetes
- Excessive Thirst
- Frequent Urination
- Weight Loss while Food Maintained
- Fatigue
- Sudden Blindness from Cataracts
- Vomiting
- Skin Lesions

When therapies are utilized a constant check on the blood sugar levels are vital.

Nutrition

A homemade diet, a raw food diet or one of the natural human grade foods are needed. *No commercial food should be involved.* Large amounts of fiber are also needed.

Lightly steamed vegetables as carrots, pea pods, string beans, broccoli, yams, watercress, asparagus, celery, parsnips, dandelion and Jerusalem artichoke hearts are very beneficial. Tofu is also beneficial.

Fiber sources include rye, millet, oats, barley, quinoa, bulghur and wheat bran. Cook one and add some vanilla, yogurt and a vegetable for a delicious meal. Additional products include lychee berries, cedar berries and blueberry leaf tea (helps decrease blood sugar levels 1 -2 times daily, must be on a regular basis). They benefit the beta cells in the pancreas.

SUPPLEMENTS

Vitamin E	to 400iu
Chromium Picolinate	to 150mcg
CoQ10	to 40mg
Oxygen Therapy	Homozoan 1/4 tsp in food (based on bodyweight).
Magnesium	to 200mg
Pantothenic Acid	to 15mg
Vitamin B Complex	to 60mg
Ester C complex	to 1500mg
Zinc	to 10mg
Manganese	to 3mg
Trace Minerals	Per label
Vitamin A	10,000 iu
Enzymes	eNZYmesPro+, Diatrol (Donsbach)
Potassium	to 5 mg
Lipoic Acid	to 25mg

Coconut Water (from immature fruit) is high in potassium and minerals. Very beneficial! Black plum helps with excessive thirst, decreasing sugar in the urine and benefiting itchy skin. Dilute in water and administer 8-15 drops up to three times daily.

HERBS

Bitter Melon	Pancreas helper, Helps produce insulin.
Jambolan	Pancreas helper (thirst symptoms), Carminative.
Gymnema	Normalizes blood sugar levels. Large quantities of white urine, immense thirst, "Sugar Killer."
Divi-Divi	Tonic.
Bilberry	Contains chromium, anti-diabetic effect.
Mountain Ash Berry	Kidney diseases and diabetes, Vitamin C deficiency.
Reed Herb	Vitamin A, vitamin C, B1-B2.
Alfalfa	Contains chlorophyll, very nutritious.
Prodigiosa	Lowers blood sugar level.
Yarrow	Helps liver and kidney function. Vitamins A, C, E, F and manganese, copper, potassium, iodine and iron.

Devils Club	Substantially lowers blood sugar. Natural substitute for insulin.
Huckleberry leaves	Helps control blood sugar.
Schizandra	Nourishes kidneys.
Turmeric	Antioxidant, anti-inflammatory, anti-hepatoxic.
Pedra Caa	"Vegetable Insulin" eliminates sugar from urine.
Stevia	Lowers blood sugar.
Shardunikha	Destroyer of sugar, controls blood sugar levels.
Uva-Ursi	All kidney & bladder problems. Diabetes.
Pata De Vaca	Helps balance sugar levels, blood cleanser

The above herbs may be bought in various combinations from local establishments.

Matabazoan is a prepared combination that supports the pancreas; helps normalize the body's response to blood sugar fluctuations and increases enzyme production. Available through Bio Energetics.

HOMEOPATHY

• *Syzygium 3x, 30c* concerns urination with high sugar content.

- *Insulin 15c* restores ability to store glycogen in liver. Skin problems.
- *Uranium Nit. 30c* pale and milky looking urine.
- *Pancreas 7c*
- *Phaseolus 15c* lowers blood sugar levels.
- *Telakucha 3x* for mellitus and insipidus, depression, skin problems and weakness. Greenish mucous in stool. Profuse urination.

CHAPTER NINE:
FLEAS, CHIGGERS, MITES AND LICE

The summer brings out the fleas. Unfortunately, battling fleas with toxic collars can bring more damage to the animal than the flea. Flea problems affect a great many dogs. Many individuals are starting to realize that flea collars not only aren't effective, but also contain chemical poisons that can affect the animal's health.

Natural flea collars are easy to make. Simply add a few drops of cedarwood, lemongrass and bergamot on the animal's regular collar. Re-apply the oils every seven to 10 days. Don't use pennyroyal, as it may cause abortions.

"Tombstone" Flea Eliminator is a natural product from Great Life Performance Pet Products utilizing organic aloe vera, borates and essential oils.

Chiggers are immature forms of mites. Usually found in the outermost part of the ear canal, they are very difficult to see with the naked eye and are a cause of extreme itching for an animal. Flea products will kill chiggers.

Cheyletiella Dermatitis is a skin problem caused by mites. Nicknamed "traveling dandruff," the skin looks scaly, crusty and moves. Mites are on the larger size and can be easily seen, mainly affecting puppies and young adolescent dogs. They can be killed with flea products.

Lice are rare in North America.

A healthy dog has a greater chance of warding off or making the episodes less severe than an immune-compromised animal. A dog fed a good natural diet with added zinc, primrose or borage oil, B-1, B-5, and Kyolic garlic has a greater resistance to fleas.

Flea Bites are annoying and itchy. On the onset of scratching, combine Aloe Vera juice, lavendin and everlasting and spray on the affected area.

Your indoor environment needs to be thoroughly cleaned and all pet bedding should be washed with 5 drops of eucalyptus, bergamot or lemongrass in the water. A good shampoo comes from cutting up five lemons, four oranges and two grapefruit into thin sections and adding them to a quart of spring water. Boil it down. Use all of the fruit in the water. Turn off the heat and let the mixture sit overnight. In the morning, strain, then add 3 oz. of Aloe Vera juice and shampoo as you usually would.

For carpets, there is an EPA-approved product called Flea Eliminator that guarantees the product against fleas for a year. Sprinkle the powder on carpets, bedding, couches, cabinets, drapes and other areas.

SPRAY

A good herbal spray consists of 1 tablespoon of natural borates, 5 drops of cedarwood, citronella and lavender in 6 oz. of aloe vera juice and 2 oz. of spring water. Shake in the bottle, comb the animal's hair backwards and spray well on the pet. In some cases, I've witnessed fleas hopping off the pet while some died immediately.

This herbal flea powder is easy to make and quite effective. Combine powdered chrysanthemum flowers, cypress, yarrow, bay, rosemary, wormwood and lemongrass. Comb the animal's hair "backward" and apply the powder.

HOMEOPATHIC REMEDIES

- *Apis Mel*   6c
- *Rhus Tox*   15c
- *Ledum*   15c

CHAPTER TEN:
IMMUNE SYSTEM

The overall health of an animal depends on a properly functioning immune system. No other system in the body is working in high gear as often as the immune system. Animals' immune systems are being bombarded entirely too often for the animal to remain healthy. Pat Frederick, DVM states, "There's been a 67% rise in cancer patients."

Let's explore a simple excursion in the park. Animals have sweat glands in their feet. If the animal walks through an area of the park that has had a pesticide or insecticide application, the animal can absorb the toxins through its paws.

• Air pollution, inhalant allergies	Immune System Activation.
• Commercial pet food with chemicals	Immune System Activation.
• Environmental toxins	Immune System Activation.
• Vaccinations	Immune System Activation.
• Water impurities	Immune System Activation.
• Stress	Immune System Activation.
• Heavy metal toxins	Immune System Activation

The immune system responds to any deviation from normal, healthy criteria. A weakened immune system opens the gateway to illness. Is it any wonder that dogs are living sicker lives?

There's a vicious cycle that needs to be broken in order to increase our animals' well being, starting from the breeder giving proper foods and ultimate nutrition to bitches. Cheap pricing and million-dollar marketing campaigns for inferior foods should not fool pet owners. Stop the over-medicating of animals. Break the cycle.

The starting point is not trying to rid all the problems at once. This can have dire effects. An old saying "Build a little, cleanse a little" is a good rule to follow.

NUTRITIONAL SUPPORT

Enzymes	eNZYmesPro+, Wobenzyme
Colloidal Silver	American Biologics, Earths Bounty
Vitamin/Mineral/Antioxidant supplement	Ultra Multi-Plex (American Biologics).
Anti-Oxidant	Forte Miller, American Biologics
Daily Essential	Doctors Finest Pet Products
Oxygen Supplement	Homozoan or Oxy-Cleanse (Earths Bounty)

Acidophilus	per label
Essential Fatty Acids	1-2 teaspoons
CO-Q-10	to 40mg
Grape Seed Extract	to 100mg
Zinc	to 10mg

Start with a good herbal de-tox system cleanser such as Power (Ejuva), Detoxaid (Biospec), or Envirozoan (Bio-Energetics). Change to a quality food. Gradually add higher amounts of the new food into the old until fully changed. Check stool consistency.

Prior to the animal eating, give it enzyme supplements such as, eNZYmesPro+ or PHD. Utilize naturally pure water add Oxy Doc (a little noni or aloe in water is beneficial).

Add 1-2 teaspoons of Barcleans organic flax seed oil to food and 4 drops colloidal silver (5pp, once daily) or Grizzly Salmon Oil. Feed animal 2-3 times daily (spreading the food out helps the digestive system).

Chop up some fresh, pesticide- and insecticide-free green vegetables or use a super green mix. Follow the label directions. Add acidophilus or organic plain yogurt, again per the label directions.

One of my favorite all-around items is Aloe Vera juice. Aloe Vera has an incredible number of health benefits.

HERBAL IMMUNE BUILDING MIXES

- 1 part each Astragalus or suma, echinacea, shizandra, dyers woad, burdock, una de gato, 1/8 part gingko biloba, 1/8 part milk thistle and 1/16 part cinnamon.

- 1 part Echinacea, turkey tail, maitake, agaricus, 1/4 part green tea, burdock, 1/8 part alfalfa, yellow dock, and 1/16 part St. John's wort, cinnamon.

- Black Walnut Hulls can be added to either.

- Boiled spring water needed for mixes. Add organic chicken or beef bouillon for flavor. These formulas can also be made into pills (add bee pollen).

- Illumination is a wonderful combination of Amazon botanicals designed to help build overall health. Available from Bio-Energetics.

- Anti-Bio is available through Crystal Star.

HERBS

Larex	Superior immune enhancer
Bee propolis w/larex	Enhances immune activity. Eclectic
System Strength	Crystal Star
Suma	
Astragalus	
Yerba Mate	
Una De Gato	
Echinacea (aug root)	
Usnea Lichen	
Purslane	High in Vitamin C, blood purifier, minerals, protein, antioxidants, and Omega 3 fatty acids.
Echinacea / Goldenseal	Freeze-dried concentrate Eclectic

HOMEOPATHIC

- *Thuja* 30C for after vaccinations
- *Echinacea* 3x is an immune enhancer

GEMMOTHERAPY

- Birch
- Rowan tree
- Honeysuckle
- Juniper

ELLIOTT HARVEY, MH

CHAPTER ELEVEN:
LIVER AND KIDNEY PROBLEMS

The largest organ in the body is the liver. This filtration and biochemical system is called upon to perform a myriad of tasks. The liver regulates blood sugar, cleanses toxins, converts vitamins and minerals (forms vitamin A from carotene, stores vitamins A and E, as well as iron and copper, and utilizes vitamin K to help coagulate the blood) into proper assimilation forms, metabolizes fats, oxidizes fatty acids, controls estrogen regulation, provides heat for the body, manufactures proteins and assists in enzyme production.

The animal's liver is constantly working to clean air pollution, chemical pollution, household chemical odors, paint odors, chemical fertilizers, food additives, chemicals in foods and dyes, cigarette smoke, viral-parasitic infestations, heavy metals, insecticides, antibiotics, medicines, chemotherapy and steroids from the body. The liver is being overtaxed on a daily basis. With our chemically induced environment, the possibility of liver and kidney failure is always present.

SIGNS OF LIVER PROBLEMS
- Orange mucous membrane
- Yellowish eyes
- Chalky or orange looking stools
- Lethargic, bloated abdomen
- Painful seizures
- Excessive water intake
- Fatigue
- Vomiting

The final phase of metabolism requires urine elimination. The kidneys are needed to excrete urine. Retention of urine, causing a "backup" in the system, leads to toxic blood, or uremia. The elimination organs are constantly being strained and compromised.

SIGNS OF KIDNEY PROBLEMS
- Vomiting
- Diarrhea
- Ammonia breath
- Brittle coat
- Lack of appetite
- Lethargy
- Blood loss
- Shock
- Heart failure

Urine color is instrumental in determining the health of the liver, gallbladder and kidneys. Blood in urine signals organ bleeding, cloudy urine indicates an infection while dark brown urine is a sign of jaundice.

LIVER NUTRIENTS

The first step is to provide a preservative free diet or raw food diet (preferred) with spring water and one tablespoon of Noni juice.

Vitamin B12	up to 250mg
Enzymes/Probiotic	Great Life Performance Pet Products
Oxygen	Oxy-caps (Earths Bounty), Homozoan (Oxy-Therapies)
B-Vitamins	to100mg
Super Green Foods	per label
Folic Acid	to 50mcg
Egg Lecithin	to 250mg
Kyolic Garlic	per label
Desiccated Liver or Raw glandular extracts	American Biologics
Positive Health	Great Life Performance Pet Products

HERBS

Blood Cleansing herbs are always utilized. Some of the most often used are red clover, burdock, celery seed, comfrey, oregon grape, dandelion and yellow dock.

Lipotropic tablets with milk thistle	Eclectic (vitamin-mineral-herb formula)
Milk Thistle	to 30mg
Bupleurum	to 20mg
Raw Glandular Extract	American Biologics
Hepa Clear	Donsbach
Milk Thistle/Dandelion combination	Eclectic
Boldo	
Tayuya	
Chanca Piedra	
Dandelion	
Liverwort	
Blessed Thistle	
Gentian	
Carqueja	
Jatoba	
Artichoke	
Fedegoso	
Zu Ling Mushroom	
Black or Blue Reishi Mushroom	
Honey Mushroom	

Envirozoan from Bio-Energetics cleanses and stimulates the liver and gallbladder, promotes detoxification and flushes and cleans the kidneys.

HOMEOPATHICS

- *Chelidonium 3x* for jaundice, pain in liver, mucous membrane yellow, urine foamy, chalky colored stools, may vomit.

- *Liver 6c* from Celletech, Dolisos

- *Bryonnia 12c* for inflamed liver, extended abdomen, hard stools, dry coughing.

- *Natrum Sulf 15c* for painful urination, enlarged liver, melancholy, watery stools.

- *Merc 30c* for yellow tongue and eyes, bad breath, sensitivity to touch.

- *Lycopodium 7c* for abdomen bloated after small meal, liver delicate to touch, stool hard, strainful urination, constipation may be present.

- *Rohitaka 6x, 15c* for liver and spleen disorders, foul smelling breath.

KIDNEY NUTRIENTS

Blood cleansing herbs are valuable (see Liver). Utilize Enzymes/ Probiotics, organic unsweetened cranberry juice or cranberry capsules. Watermelon seeds and fresh fruit (apples, pears) are beneficial.

Vitamin B Complex	to 50mg
Vitamin C with Bioflavonoids	to 1000mg daily
Vitamin E	to 400 iu daily

HERBS

For herbal soup, combine 1 part parsley, 1 part celery, 1 part red clover,
1 part hollyhock, 1 part uva ursi, 1 part dandelion, and1 part holy thistle. Add organic chicken or beef bouillon cube.

Put ingredients in glass pot (never aluminum) and add bottled water. Bring to a light boil, strain and add stevia or honey to sweeten.

Cool, then use 1/2 cup, 2-3 times daily, administering orally. Refrigerate the unused portion, but be sure to use the balance within two days.

HOMEOPATHIC

- *Berberis Vulg 12x* for extreme pain, urine bright red, frequent urination, slimy urine with mucous.

- *Aconite 30c* for kidney failure, nervous, painful urination, urine red, fever, thirst.

- *Cantharsis 15c* for frequent urge to pass urine, scant amounts.

- *Solidago Virga 3x* for reddish-brown urine, difficult urination, albumen, blood and slime in urine. Offensive-smelling urine.

- *Petroselinum 3x* for frequent urination, intense itching, burning in uretha, milky discharge.

- *Kidney 7c* available from Celletech, Dolisos

- *Natrum Mur 6c* for urination difficulty.

GEMMOTHERAPY
- Ash tree
- Juniper
- Birch
- Olive tree
- Rosemary (liver-gallbladder and mild kidney drainage)
- Black Honeysuckle
- Elm
- Malze

ELLIOTT HARVEY, MH

CHAPTER TWELVE:
QUESTIONS AND ANSWERS

Question: My dog constantly licks her paw, sometimes until it is hairless and sore. What is the problem?

Answer: Paw licking can be attributed to either allergies or a bacterial infection. A term for this is *Lick Granuloma*. Dogs have sweat glands in their paws. A minor fleabite can initiate licking until a sore develops, followed by redness and hair loss.

Here's an itch-relief formula: to 4 oz Aloe Vera Gel, add neem, echinacea and Oregon grape. Mix 1/8 oz of each powdered herb into the gel and apply liberally. For bacterial infections, use a liquid mix containing echinacea, golden seal and neem. An allergy may cause skin licking (see Allergy chapter).

Proper nutrition should always be maintained. OxyDoc can also be used to treat the bacterial infection.

Q: I've been told that enzymes are good for my dog. Can you tell me the benefits of enzymes and if my dog gets enough in his kibble?

A: *Every* bio-chemical action in the body

utilizes enzymes. Enzymes are the catalysts for all vitamins, hormones, amino acids and minerals. Nothing in the system can be accomplished without enzyme activity; they're considered the catalysts of life.

Enzymes are classified to function: *Digestive* (secreted in the digestive tract to break down food, allows absorption into bloodstream), *Metabolic* (to enhance chemical breakdown within the cells for detoxification and energy) and *Antioxidant* (for the destruction of toxins and free radicals in the liver and bloodstream).

Enzymes are heat sensitive; they burn off at 118 F. Commercial pet foods are processed in an extruder, with temperatures exceeding 300 F. Animals are not receiving beneficial enzymes for absorption, utilization and assimilation of vital nutrients.

An enzyme supplement from Great Life Performance Pet Products (eNZYmes Pro +), PHD is essential additions for overall health. A raw food diet provides enough natural enzymes to digest their own nutrients. Any food cooked or processed lacks the naturally occurring enzymes that help counter many ailments.

Commercial and cooked foods provoke the body to utilize its limited stored enzymes to aid in digestion causing additional damage. Using the body's backup supply of stored enzymes diminishes the its capacity to aid other essential functions in the body. Enzymes have been shown to help the immune system and combat digestive disorders, poor coat, excessive shedding, skin problems, joint ailments, weight problems, allergies, lethargy, organs, bloat, flatulence and excrement eating.

DIGESTIVE ENZYMES

- Amylase- reduces the molecular structure of starches for better absorption into blood stream.
- Protease- enhances protein utilization to usable peptides and amino acids.
- Cellulase- Breaks down the fiber portion of food for maximum utilization.
- Lipase- Acts as an agent to breakdown fats and lipids for enzyme activity and maximizes fat-soluble vitamins.
- Pectinase- Crucial for cell growth and development. Maintains water balance.
- Phytase- Breaks down hydric acid for better absorption of minerals.
- Lactase-Helps break down lactose.
- Xylanase- Helps breakdown fiber.
- Hemicellulase- Breaks down plant structure for easier digestion
- Alpha-Galactosidase-Helps break down carbohydrates.
- Invertase- helps break down sucrose.

Each enzyme has its own specific function.

Bill Pollack, DVM believes cutting out commercial foods and providing proper nutrition and enzyme enhancement to the animal can avoid the majority of illnesses.

Q: My dog constantly gets cuts when we walk. Is there something natural I can use on the cuts?

A: Yes. Here's a good general topical to use. To Aloe Vera Gel, add 10 drops each of the following extracts: Echinacea (aug. fol. root), myrrh, burdock and tea tree oil. Clean and dry the pad or foot with hydrogen peroxide before applying the gel.

Q: What about those new "Power Bars" and the treats that claim to be good for arthritis?

A: Look good; smell good and dogs love them. I've reviewed many of them. Some are actually pretty good. Read the label carefully. Some may have excessive sugars or toxic preservatives

I noticed a semi-moist jerky bar for arthritis with wheat, beef, corn syrup, glycerin, and wheat gluten, natural smoke flavor, salt and potassium sorbate included. Don't be fooled by pretty labels. The more knowledgeable you are, the better the products will become. Ask for human grade and buy only human-grade products without preservatives.

Here's a real life horror story: I was at a trade show where I visited a booth selling chicken and turkey smoked treats. I asked the representative/owner if the meat was human grade:

Representative: It comes from an FDA plant.
EH: So, the meat is human grade.
Representative: Not really, sometimes the plant gets too hot and the meat becomes contaminated, the FDA doesn't allow the plant to sell it for human food.
EH: (amazed) Am I hearing you correctly? You're selling contaminated food to pets as a treat?
Representative: I've eaten it and it didn't get me sick.

Q: My dog has anemia. What causes this condition and are there any natural alternatives for treatment?

A: Anemia is caused by an underproduction of red blood cells. Many dogs will breathe harder to compensate for this problem. Increased breathing will transit oxygen rapidly through the system to help compensate for the decreased number of oxygen carrying red blood cells.

Factors that cause anemia include a B-12 deficiency, loss of blood, hemorrhage, eating rat poison, parasite infestation, infections, leukemia, worms and fleas. Dogs with anemia will show various signs such as pale mucous membrane, lethargy, and variations in breathing, weight loss, coldness, colored urine and depression.

Nutrients needed: Vitamin B 12 (may need injections if malabsorption is present). Watch out for deficiency of folic acid. If the animal is given B12 and lacks folic acid, a deficiency in folic acid will occur. The opposite is also true.

A good B-Complex is useful. Do not take iron supplements alone. This can cause an overabundance in the system. Iron can interfere with the absorption of copper, manganese, and zinc. Vitamin C enhances the body's natural ability to absorb iron from various sources. Calcium hinders iron absorption (make sure your multiple doesn't have both). Nutrients needed can be obtained from desiccated liver, blackstrap molasses, dark green vegetables, bee pollen, honey, raisins, natural unprocessed vegetable oils, safflower or wheat germ oil (vitamin E) and tofu (add a small amount of blackstrap molasses). Kelp contains iodine. Dulse, nori and wakame are useful.

Q: My dog is getting older and is having urination problem. He doesn't want to get up to go outside to urinate in the evening. What can I do?

A: Incontinence can occur when the kidneys start degrading. Walk him more often throughout the day. If his normal procedure is once, try 3-4 times daily. If he's arthritic, it may be painful to rise. Dogs with urinary problems may have a bacterial infection in the bladder. Try 2-3 teaspoons of organic (unsweetened) cranberry juice over a week's time. Black elder extract is also useful for incontinence.

Envirozoan	Bio Energetics, helps flush and de-tox the kidneys.
System Cleanse	Doctors Finest Pet Products, helps clean system
Detox-Aid	Bio-Spec

Q: My pet's breath stinks. Does tooth brushing work?

A: Brushing kills germs in the immediate area. Bad breath is attributed to undigested food or a dental problem.

Here are a couple of suggestions:

- Change to a natural food without preservatives or chemical additives.
- Utilize enzymes prior to feeding
- A good combination to rid bad breath is 2 parts Montmorillonite clay (absorbs toxins), 1 part each of chlorophyll, senna, and peppermint. Make into capsules or pills.
- A good chew bone will help prevent plaque buildup.
- Brushing helps remove bacteria buildup in the mouth. Utilize natural toothpaste that incorporate Neem Oil, and various other natural herbal antibacterial ingredients.
- Add a probiotic supplement onto the toothpaste, in the food or in the daily water.

Q: My miniature pinscher has been doing something weird. He acts like he's trying to catch flies. He looks in the air and starts snapping. His blood work looks good.

A: Sounds like your dog may be having seizures. Seizures can be attributed to an accumulation of toxins (lead), allergies, low blood sugar, brain damage or genetics.

Try an extract combination of St. Johns Wort (3 drops), gingko biloba (3 drops),

Oregon grape (3 drops), blue cohosh (2 drops), bupleurum (2 drops), sarsaparilla (2 drops) and stevia (1/2 drop), plus 1/8 teaspoon of Homozoan (to food). B-Vitamins are necessary. You can also try Calm Dog from Doctors Finest Pet Products.

Q: **What should we keep in a first aid kit?**

A: Thermometer (normal temperature is 101F to 102F), a heating pad or blanket (for shock, low temperature), activated charcoal (poisoning, toxins, diarrhea), sports water with electrolytes (shock, diarrhea, dehydration. a simple test – raise the skin up on the neck. if it stays up a few seconds, dehydration is setting in), mineral oil, bandages (tape and scissors), VBG anti-diarrhea gel, flashlight, hydrogen peroxide, injury salve, solution of eyebright for eye problems, tincture of chamomile, arnica 15c, cotton swaps and tweezers.

Q: **My German shepherd has developed diarrhea. The veterinarian said he has too much bacteria in his small intestine. She gave him some medication but that hasn't helped. What is causing this and what can I use to stop the diarrhea?**

A: Diarrhea can be from a variety or reasons as: change in diet, over eating, poor quality food, ingestion of various toxic substances. The medication may have disrupted the intestinal flora balance. VBG Anti Diarrhea Gel will stop diarrhea. Probiotic supplement can stop diarrhea.

Hold back food for 24 hours. Add a probiotic supplement, 1-4 drops kyolic garlic and 1 teaspoon of flax seed to food. If the stool is foamy, you have a bacterial infection; yellow stool means food is moving too fast in the small bowel; large gray stool is inadequate absorption.

Charcoal tablets help remove toxins. Applesauce contains pectin, which can stop mild diarrhea. Bentonite clay (Montmorillonite) help stop diarrhea, while removing toxins. Amaranth seeds can stop bloody stools and diarrhea.

HOMEOPATHIC
- *Calc. Carb 7c* for undigested food, whitish stool, watery.
- *Echinacea 3x* for bacterial infections
- *Carbo. Veg 30c* for diarrhea

Q: What kind of alternative therapy can I use on my 3 1/3-year-old with ligament damage? She's been on anti-inflammatory drugs combined with rest for four weeks with no significant improvement. My vet wants to give her injections and an operation. I feel this is a bit drastic at this stage.

A: Rest and relaxation is paramount. To relieve the inflammation, try Colostrum and a mixture of golden seal and echinacea (burdock, turmeric, ginger in the mix work well). Apply a wrap containing Aloe Vera Gel with 4-8 drops of arnica and 1-3 drops cayenne. Replace the wrap 2-3 times daily.

Q: My dog went with me on a trip. When we returned he became constipated. What should I do?

A: Constipation may have been caused by:
- Eating a rock or other item. Object may have caused a blockage.
- Stress, lack of fiber, different food.

First, if animal is eating add some mineral oil or aloe vera or canola oil or psyllium to the meal. This will flush out an object. Don't go more than two days. Rapid Paste from Great Life Performance Pet Products is beneficial and fast acting.

If normal movement hasn't started, a severe blockage may have occurred. If movement occurs, add a probiotic supplement to meal. This will help balance the intestinal flora in the colon.

Q: For 12 months we've been trying to heal a small puncture wound in our dogs paw. The vet put him on an antibiotic/

anti-inflammatory medication orally for months. We soak it daily but it won't heal. We put a sock on it when she's outside. What can we do naturally?

A: Try a mixture of aloe vera gel, usnea lichen, burdock, myrrh, and mullein and some liquid sea minerals. Make sure to cover the above with a wrap and sock when going outdoors. Clean the paw with 3% hydrogen peroxide (food grade) before using mix.

A combination of Aloe Vera 2 oz, 6oz Spring Water and 4 drops each of Tea Tree, Myrrh and Lavender works well.

Q: What can I give my stressed out dog?

A: First, figure out why the animal is stressed out. Has there been any dramatic change in his life? Look at his mucous membranes (check other question) to see if he's having some physical problem. Has his activity level changed? Any changes in food or eating habits? Do an activity with him that he loves and see if he's changed. Is he limping or hunched over? Can you notice if he's in pain of any sorts. It's easy to give a calming agent but you need to find the underlying cause.

You can try Calm Dog from Doctors Finest Pet Products or a combination utilizing St. Johns Wort (not to be used with prescription medicine), passionflower, hops (has b-vitamins), chamomile and extra b-vitamins.

Q: I have a border collie. She has problems with bites on the tips of her ears. I've tried to treat them unsuccessfully. What can I put on her ears to relieve the problem and keep the flies off?

A: First, you can add some kyolic garlic to the food. Second, mix the following essential oils together in some aloe vera gel or jojoba oil, dab on ear: cedarwood, lemongrass, tea tree or neem oil.

Q: My dog has been diagnosed with Cushing's disease. Are there any alternative therapies for this?

A: Cushing's disease is a hormonal problem. The adrenal gland is producing too much cortisol. Prescription medications, ear medications, eye drops and skin creams containing cortisone can lead to this problem. Cushing's Disease has been known to have a high occurrence in the brain. A tumor in the pituitary gland can be attributed to Cushing's disease. Licorice contains natural cortisone.

The B-Vitamin group is needed. 1/4 teaspoon of Homozoan (oxygenates the brain and system), astragalus (aids adrenal gland function), gingko biloba, yellow dock (aids liver function), echinacea (blood purifier, antibiotic), usnea lichen (antibiotic), kelp, slippery elm (assists adrenal gland function), borage oil, codonopsis and vitex (helps pituitary gland) are all quite useful. A natural hydrocortisone derived from soy is also available.

Q: My dog is having breathing problems. What can be attributed to this?

A: Breathing problems can mean a leaking heart valve, enlarged heart, lung disease, collapsed trachea, anemia, shock, internal bleeding, cancer, poisoning, bloat, heartworms, or pneumonia. All of these are considered life threatening.

Q: I've heard various stories regarding vaccines. Can they have side effects?

A: Jody Kincaid, DVM gives animals that receive vaccinations a homeopathic nosode or Thuja to lower possible side effects. Vaccinations can make the immune system go crazy. Many Veterinarians feel that vaccinations and booster shots need be re-evaluated. Many animals are experiencing adverse reactions to vaccines.

- Thuja 30C
- eNZYmes Pro +
- Positive Health

Prepare the animal with homeopathic preparations or eNZYmes Pro + five days prior to vaccination, after vaccination continue for a few more days. Celletech also makes a protocol for helping prevent adverse side effects.

Q: My dog keeps dragging his rectum on the ground. What can be the cause of this?

A: There are various reasons for this. Odor and licking at the rectum could mean an infection. Bowel difficulty in males may mean a hernia; blood licking at the anus or hardness around the anus could indicate a tumor. Blood discharge and fever can signify abscess. Rectal itch can be from worms. Allergies also can impact the anal gland.

Q: What does looking at a dog's mucous membranes indicate?

A: Membranes tell us many conditions of a dog, as does tongue diagnosis. Mucous membranes found when you raise the lips should be bright pink/pinky red. Mucous membranes should be moist. A dry, sticky membrane can mean shock or circulation problems.

Various colors are signs of illness:
- *White membranes-pale pink- gray* = Anemia, fleas, zinc toxicity, bone marrow disease, worms, poisoning, shock, endocrine problem, heart problem, hemophilia, trauma, hemorrhage. This is a serious problem.
- *Yellow to Orange* = Liver (jaundice), pancreatic, gallbladder.
- *Blue-Purple* = Carbon monoxide poisoning, asthma, pneumonia, cardiovascular system, poison. Again, a serious problem.
- *Dark Red* = Bacterial infection.
- *Muddy Red* = Circulation problem.
- *Bright Red* = Gingivitis, hypothermia, poison, stomatitis.
- *Brown Tongue* = Kidney disease.

Remember, some dogs have black mouths and tongues naturally.

Q: Our dog seems to be getting extremely lethargic and depressed. We're getting very worried.

A: There is an abundance of reasons for a dog to get lethargic. Pain is always present. His system is having a problem in an area. Possible reasons include arthritis, cancer or pancreatic (diarrhea, vomiting), infection (fever), kidney or liver problem (excessive thirst and urination) or heart problems (breathing problem). Any and all of these problems need immediate attention.

Q: We're noticing some blood in our dog's urine.

A: Blood in the urine can be attributed to a bladder infection (stones), cancer (can be bleeding in other areas also), hepatitis, and liver disease or poisoning. A reaction to prescription medications is another possibility.

Q: What is kennel cough? Is it treatable?

A: Kennel cough is a contagious air borne disease attributed to both viral and bacterial conditions. It's treatable with herbal antibiotic formulas (see Immune chapter). Kennel cough can be attributed to a low immune system, stress and confined conditions. A harsh cough is present. Small dogs and puppies need to paid close attention to prevent pneumonia. A drop of essential oil of peppermint / eucalyptus is helpful on their collar. OxyDoc is also effective against kennel cough from Great Life Performance Pet Products.

Q: How can we get rid of ringworm?
A: Ringworm is a fungal infection. This highly contagious fungus can be passed

on to other animals as well as to humans. Circular bald patches occur, but itching is not a prerequisite. Vesicular eruptions or scabbed skin (approximately _" in diameter) may be observed in the head, neck and legs. Ridding an animal of ringworm requires the animal having a healthy immune system. A good natural diet is needed with additional Vitamin C, a multiple supplement, and enzymes.

Remedies include two tablespoons of lime juice or apple cider vinegar and 10 drops each of the following extracts: black walnut hulls, tea tree or neem, garlic (optional) in the liquid. Apply to area 2-3 times daily. It can also be used internally. Cypress is also effective against ringworm and skin fungal infections. OxyDoc is very effective.

HOMEOPATHIC
- *Bacillinum 200c, 1M,* Ringworm. Infrequent dosages.
- *Chrysarobinum 6c,* Crusty Stage, Eruptions around face, Ringworm.
- *Bel Fruit 3x, 30x*   Itching, Ringworm.

Q: Does my dog really need to have his teeth checked?

A: Yes. Dogs get periodontal disease just as we do. If a dog's mouth is not checked, certain afflictions can occur, including gingivitis (soft tissue inflammation), broken tooth (may be attributed to feeding real bones as treats, pain, behavioral problems), osteomyelitis (deep bone infection), bad breath and periodontal disease (teeth grinding, mouth not being opened or closed completely, rejecting hard kibble, face and mouth rubbing).

Q: Our dog is constantly eating his stool. We've tried placing hot pepper sauce on it to stop him from eating it. Is there anything else we can put on it to stop him?

A: Your dog is trying to tell you that something is missing in his diet, he's not absorbing nutrients correctly or he's stressed out. Some young dogs eat stools as a learning experience and stop. Older dogs sometimes eat dirt, wood, grass, or other strange items.

- Change the food to a preservative free, natural product. He may not be able to breakdown the commercial food.
- *Add digestive (plant based) enzymes to his meal.* This is a very crucial item.
- Many ailments disappear utilizing enzymes. eNZYmesPro+ is highly effective.
- He may not be producing enough hydrochloric acid, add one teaspoon of apple cider vinegar (per 30 pounds) into the food.

141

Q: How can we get rid of "Hot Spots"?

A: Skin ailments, including dermatitis, would be less severe, or removed all together, if we would get away from chemicals, preservatives and environmental pollutants. Food allergies from poor quality kibble are a continuing source of skin problems. The animal's elimination system is extremely overtaxed trying to rid the body of toxins. When the epidermal layer secretes an excessive amount of toxins, skin problems develop.

Change to a high-grade, preservative free diet (Great Life Performance Pet Foods) or raw food diet. Eliminate all allergenic items including dog treats. Use high-grade treats such as Canidae baked biscuits (see manufacturers list). Fast the animal for up to 48 hours. Use only bottled water.

HERBS

Detoxification of the system is a priority. Use blood-cleansing herbs such as echinacea, golden seal, burdock, comfrey, dandelion, garlic, kelp, Oregon grape and red clover (see chapters on Liver and Kidney, Immune System and Alternative Therapies).

Add enzymes to the food	eNYZmes Pro+
Daily Essential	Doctors Finest Pet Products
Organic flax seed oil	2 -3 teaspoons daily
B-Complex with amino acids	90mg daily.
Zinc	15mg daily
Kelp	1-2 tablets, or 1 teaspoon 2 times daily
Healthy skin	Biospec
For thyroid problem	Michaels Thyroid Factors, or Coconut oil

- Green tea: wait until cool, and then apply to skin. Helps soothe irritated skin
- "Totally Cool" Hot Spot Relief Spray Great Life Performance Pet Products

For external detoxification, mix into O2 Spray (Earths Bounty or Donsbach) or Aloe Vera Juice, 3 drops each of essential oils of bergamot, carrot seed, neem and chamomile. Other options include: clary sage and cedarwood. Spray as often as needed.

Change to a natural (no synthetic chemicals), preservative-free shampoo. Add an additional 1/4-cup aloe vera juice to the shampoo. You can utilize the same essential oils into the shampoo as above.

HOMEOPATHIC
- *Sulphur*15c-30c
- *Graphites* 15c-30c
- *Rhus Tox* 30c

Q: Are mushrooms beneficial?

A: Many individuals do not realize how wonderful mushrooms actually are. They have marvelous medicinal qualities. The most commonly known are maitake, reishi and cordyceps. However there are a host of others that are gaining more attention.

Mushrooms have been used for centuries as culinary and medicinally for centuries. They have very low toxicity and can be used a high doses. Two terms are used when describing a mushroom: *Mycelium*, are the cells that produce the mushrooms. *Fruit bodies* are the mature full mushrooms. Beta-glucans and Polysaccharides have been discovered as having immune enhancing and tumor fighting (activating NK-Killer cells) properties. I am a strong proponent of mushroom therapies.

All mushrooms are not the same. Organic grown mushrooms will not have any of the possible toxins or heavy metals that commercial varieties may contain and are grown in a clean air and water environment. I have been fortunate to discuss and coordinate remedies with Paul Stamets,

David Law and Jeff Chilton.

SOME MUSHROOMS AND BENEFITS

- *Agaricus Blazei* -(Murrill, Sun) Cancer fighter (highest level of beta-glucans and activates NK cells), anti-tumor, immune booster, anti-viral, antibacterial. Used for: tumors, chronic diarrhea, diabetes, rheumatism, and cystitis.
- *Reishi* -Anti-oxidant, immune booster, antibacterial, anti-tumor/viral, increased oxygen absorption, cholesterol lowering, yeast infections. Used for: Leukemia, liver tumor (hepatoma), arthritis, diabetes, radiation / chemotherapy therapy (cell regenerative effect and cell protector), hepatitis, allergenic (inhibits histamine release). Works as a liver and kidney detoxifier.
- *Cordyceps* -Anti-tumor, immune booster, cholesterol reducing, endurance, liver and kidney fortifier. Used for: Lung cancer, leukemia, hepatitis, lymphoma, nerve problems, renal failure, anemia, and helps build bone marrow.
- *Maitake* -Anti-tumor (mammary), anti-diabetic, immune booster anti-viral. Used for: Mammary cancer, diabetes, prostate cancer, lung problems,

arthritis and anti-parasitic properties. Helps relieve the side effects of chemotherapy.

- *Zhu Ling* -Anti-tumor, antibiotic, anti-inflammatory, liver helper, diuretic. Used for: Lung, bladder, liver cancer, leukemia, after radiation / chemotherapy use, urinary tract infections. Strengthens kidneys, spleen.
- *Turkey Tail* -Anti-oxidant, boosts NK cell activity, anti-tumor, anti-bacterial, anti-viral, immune modulator, acts directly on tumor cells, boosts cellular immunity. Used for: Adjunct to chemotherapy, cervical, lung, esophagus, colon, sarcoma, melanoma, fibrosarcoma, carcinoma and other cancers, leukemia, diabetes.
- *Lions Mane* -Nerve growth stimulator, antimicrobial, anti-tumor, immune modulator. Used for: Gastritis, stomach ailments, cancer (GI tract) and improvement of muscle/motor response.
- *Shitake*-Liver helper, immune modulator (increases nk killer cells), strong anti-viral and anti-tumor properties, lentinen stimulates lymphocytes and immune helpers, activates bone marrow cells. Used for: Virus, cholesterol reduction, and cancer.

- *Oyster* - Anti-tumor, cholesterol lowering, 8 essential amino acids, Vitamins B1, B2, B5, B6, B7, P, Essential Fatty Acids, Fiber, Lipids, Protein, Minerals, depending on the growth medium. Iron. Used for: Blood Strengthener (anemia), mammary tumors, sarcoma, cholesterol lowering.
- *Chaga-* Anti-tumor, Appetite stimulator, pain reduction. Used for: Cancer-mammary, GI tract, cervical.
- *Iceman-* anti-parasitic

Q: My dog has Irritable Bowel Syndrome. What is it and what alternative methods are there?

A: Irritable bowel is an irritation in the lining of the bowels. Also referred to as nervous diarrhea. Improper muscular contraction for digestion leads to food and toxin and mucous accumulation. This causes interference in the flowing of materials in the digestive tract.

The accumulation can lead to parasites, viral and bacterial growth. Causes maybe food allergies, improper nutritional food or stress. Veterinarians are observing this disorder in increasing numbers.

Nutrition

A good high fiber diet is required. Brown rice, Flax seed, Oats should be utilized. Increased amounts of Vitamin A, E, Selenium, and Aloe Vera juice one to two times daily.

Herbs

Canadian fleabane	Tincture
Grapefruit seed extract	Per label
Fiberzoan, Arcozoan	Bio-Energetics
eNZYmes Pro +	Great Life Performance Pet Products
Larex w/ propolis	Eclectic
Positive Health	Great Life Performance Pet Products

Additionally, cinnamon bark relieves diarrhea and gastrointestinal disorders. Loosestrife also relieves diarrhea.

HOMEOPATHIC
- *Colchicum: 7c* for watery stools, frequent pain.
- *Argentum Nit: 7c* for diarrhea alternating with constipation, mucous in stool, flatulence.
- *Kali Phos: 7c* for blood in the stool, putrid smelling stools, worried, stools maybe yellow.

Q: I have a small dog that should weigh about 18 pounds. Right now he weighs 25 pounds. I have reduced his daily intake of food and increased his exercise. Is there anything else I can try? He doesn't seem to be losing weight.

A: Simply reducing his food is the easy out. Is the animal's pituitary gland / thyroid acting properly? Is the food too hard to digest? Are you using a commercial kibble or canned food? Are you incorporating enzymes / probiotics? Has the dog had any medications or shots lately?

There maybe several underlying causes for the weight gain. Here are some weight loss suggestions:
- Change to a preservative free home cooked or raw food diet.
- For Gland Problems, add one teaspoon of kelp to meal and /or one capsule of Michaels Thyroid Factors

- Glandular extract from American Biologics.
- Continue to exercise
- eNZYmes Pro+ (Great Life Performance Pet Products), Unleash (PHD)
- Coconut Oil

Supplements to Aid in Fat Reduction

- *Chromium Picolinate* supplement helps eliminate fat.
- *Garcinia* helps slow down the production of fat and aids digestion.
- *L-Carnitine* promotes metabolism of fats.
- *Hercampuri* improves production of enzymes, enhances metabolism.
- *Triphala* helps digestion and nutrient absorption. Aids metabolism.

Q: My dog's urine keeps killing my grass. What can I use so his urine stops killing or yellowing my lawn?

A: There are some products on the market that address this issue. However, on the label they have a "beware" notice stating the product may injure an internal organ. Carolyn Araiza, DVM states that the best approach is to rinse the lawn as soon as your dog urinates. Altering the pH of a dog can lead to health problems.

You can try natural probiotics to help correct the intestinal flora of the animal.

Q: What should I beware of in dog shampoos and conditioners?

A: Excellent question. Indeed there are precautions to take with these products. As with humans, warm water opens the pores of the skin. Many shampoos have synthetics, harsh chemicals, sulfates, preservatives (edta), DEA, coloring agents and fragrances (other than natural) etc. These chemicals can cause an allergic skin reaction alerting a response from the immune system.

- Fragrances including strawberry, kiwi, and citrus have produced skin reactions.
- Do not allow the animal to lick or lay in shampoo.
- If your dog's skin becomes irritated, apply cool water to skin to aid in rinsing off the chemicals. A few drops of Aloe Vera Juice can help soothe irritation.

I've noticed some labels stating botanicals, natural cleansers, essence of, herbal extracts, etc. There are no requirements for manufacturers to disclose all the ingredients on the label. Read the entire label. If you're concerned, call the company and ask for the MSDS on the product. This lists all the ingredients in the product. Since natural remedies have come into national attention, companies are trying to jump on the bandwagon adding some buzzwords to the label.

Use only shampoos that are 100% natural without chemical additives.

Q: My dog was diagnosed with mange. What is mange?

A: Mange can come in various forms. Mites are always the problem.

- *Sarcoptic* involves severe itching and discomfort as the female mite is laying her eggs beneath the skin. Usually found around elbows, paws, underside, ears, and face. The intensity of scratching can be extremely violent. Skin lesions, scabs, crusts are often observed.
- *Demodectic Mange* leads to hair loss without scratching.

Try some garlic oil, neem oil or tinctures of echinacea or usnea lichen on problem.

INFUSION

- Combine violet leaves, black walnut, lavender and lemon. Wash the problem area with solution.

HOMEOPATHIC
- ∞ Sulphur 30c helps stop itching.

Q: Is there a natural remedy for worms (parasites)?

A: Various natural remedies have been used successfully on worms. Here are some suggestions (*Note*: suggestions are not for heartworms).

Black Walnut / Wormwood Combination	Eclectic
Rascal Formula	Hanna Kroeger
VerMex	Crystal Star

A nice mix to make at home consists of two parts black walnut hulls (green), two parts wormwood, two parts ground pumpkin seeds, two parts brucea (Tung-Pei-Kuan-Chung) or carqueia, one part Aloe Vera, 10 drops kyolic garlic, one part Jackass bitters or rue, 1 part butternut bark, 1/4 part cascara sagrada, 1/4 part cloves, 1/10 part cayenne pepper and 1 part slippery elm (as a binder).

Add room temperature spring water and stir to make gruel (paste). You can add additional amounts of slippery elm to obtain proper consistency. Roll into _" (dime-size) balls and brush with flax seed oil or honey.

Give 4 to 6 balls daily to a medium-size dog. You may buy a can of pumpkin utilizing the herbs in that base.

This is another parasite mix you can make at home. Take the seeds from nine Pomegranates and nine pumpkins, seven lemons, five tangerines and five grapefruits. Dry the seed in an oven at its lowest setting for 4-6 hours. Put the seeds in a small bowl and crush into a fine powder. Give the animal up to 1/2 teaspoon in aloe vera juice with two drops of garlic on empty stomach. I have been told that feeding canned pumpkin to the animal can also get rid of worms.

- Neem leaves help expel worms.
- Vidanja is effective against tapeworm.
- Pomeganate seeds rids tapeworm.

HOMEOPATHIC PREPARATIONS

- *Kousso* is a tincture for expelling tapeworms
- *Feliz Mas* is a tincture for worm symptoms and bloat
- *Thymol 6x* for hookworm
- *Carbon Tetrachloride 3c* for hookworm

See the question below on giardia for additional information.

Q: What is Giardia? Is it a fatal disease?

A: Giardia isn't a disease; rather, it is a protozoa infestation (parasites) that causes diarrhea and stomach problems. This parasite usually infects the small intestine. Stool observation can determine if the animal has giardia. Diarrhea that is light colored and may contain mucus are symptomatic of giardia.

In normal everyday life we cannot get away from parasites. Parasites are everywhere from water sources, airborne contaminants, ground cover and food sources.

Treatment of Giardia and worms includes herbs, which work in various ways:

- *Chaparro* inhibits the growth of protozoa (anti-parasitic).
- *Boldo* kills intestinal worms and helps with digestion.
- *Carqueja* fortifies the blood and helps either kill or expel parasites.
- *Maitake* mushrooms works well against parasites.
- *Grapefruit seed extract* is good against all parasites.
- *Kyolic garlic* affects the intestinal walls.
- *Yucca* attacks the worm's outer shell, allowing system to assimilate into protein.
- *OxyDoc* helps eliminate parasites

Q: What is the normal pulse rate and temperature for a dog?

A: The average normal temperature for a dog ranges from 100.5F to 101.5F and can go up to 101.8F. The pulse rate for small dogs is approximately 70 beats per minute, while for large dogs the pulse rate can be 120 beats per minute.

Q: My dog is losing pigmentation around his nose. What can be the problem?

A: Pigmentation can be lost due to his plastic food bowl. Dogs can be allergic to certain plastics.

Change the food and water bowl. I prefer using a metal combination unit made to keep water and food off the ground. The elevation also allows for easier swallowing.

Q: What are signs of poisoning and a proper response?

A: In todays home an animal is deluged with chemicals. Household cleaners, paint, antifreeze (which has a taste dogs like), rat poison, battery acid, fertilizer, insecticides, fabric softener, pesticides, glues, pastes, chocolates, non-prescription pain relievers, OTC products and certain plants are always suspect.

A poisoned animal will show signs in fewer than two hours. His mucous membranes will turn white, pale pink or bright red. Identifying the poison is paramount. Go to a veterinarian immediately if you suspect any type of poisoning or call the Animal Poison Hotline at 1-888-232-8870.

DO NOT INDUCE VOMITING if household cleaners, paint, solvents, acids, motor oil, petroleum distillates, antifreeze or strychnine (rat poison) is involved.

Any time the central nervous system is involved, get immediate veterinary attention.

In cases where proper procedure *is* to induce vomiting (eliminating the poison in the stomach) and delay poison absorption, the following procedures apply:

A tincture of sarsaparilla is a strong blood purifier and toxin antidote. Use 40 drops in 1-cup warm water and pour it slowly into the animal's throat.

TO INDUCE VOMITING

3% Hydrogen Peroxide, the fresher the better. One milligram per pound of weight, undiluted. Apply with bulb syringe. The bubbles will induce vomiting.

POISON ABSORPTION DELAY

- Activated charcoal: 10-20 capsules in 1/2-to-one cup of warm chicken broth.

Slowly pour into mouth using a bulb syringe or baster.
- Charcoal Aid (in local stores) comes in plastic bottle mix with warm chicken broth (one gram per kilo of weight). Administer with a bulb syringe or baster.

Q: I've been hearing about EFAs. What are they?

A: The term Essential Fatty Acids refers to items that cannot be synthesized by the body. Supplementation is the only way to obtain EFAs. They are critical to the skin. EFAs helps maintain healthy skin by keeping cell membranes stable. Enzyme activity.

Benefits include strong anti-inflammatory action, protection against seborrhea, atropic dermatitis, pruritis and erthema. They help improve growth rates, immune enhancement, slow-wound healing, arthritis and cardiovascular problems and may also help against allergies and anti-inflammatory prescription medicines. Proper supplementation ratios are Omega 6 to Omega 3, 2:1 to 10:1.Wild Salmon Oil is extremely beneficial.

Q: What are probiotics and how do they work?

A: The internal system is a living ecological system inhabited with trillions of bacteria cells. The animals system contains helpful bacteria and problem bacteria in their system. This is referred to as the intestinal flora. Proper intestinal flora in the gastrointestinal tract is essential for proper digestion and keeping pathogens in check.

A delicate coexisting balance is constantly being sought. When the balance of microflora of the animal is changed due to stress, synthetics, bad food, chlorine in the water or prescription medicine, toxin-producing bacteria and fungi can achieve a strong foothold in the gastrointestinal tract disrupting the balance leading to many illness.

Not all probiotics are the same. Microencapsulated are preferred. The microorganisms are manufactured to become active in the intestinal tract. Encapsulated probiotics pass through stomach acids with a minimal loss. Extremely high and active amounts of live bacteria enter the gut.

PROBIOTICS WORK TO COMBAT:
- Diarrhea
- Intestinal Gas
- Constipation
- Allergies
- Skin Problems
- Bad Breath

- Yeast overgrowth
- Fatigue
- Compromised immune system
- Infections, including chronic degenerative diseases. Overgrowth of yeast, causing problems can be attributed to a change in the microflora.

A healthy gastrointestinal tract will: include a strong immune system; promote hormonal balance; keep harmful bacteria in check; regulate the digestive system, maintain chemical reactions; enhance vitamin, enzyme and nutrient absorption, fight cancer in the colon; is antiallergenic; antidiarrhea; and possesses antioxidant and anti-carcinogenic properties. Probiotics help keep the acid/alkaline balance in check.

PROBIOTIC LIST
- *Lactobacillus Acidophilus* - stimulates lactic acid production in the small intestine. Changes pH to a hostile environment for bad bacteria and pathogens. Helps with nutrient movement along intestinal tract. Helps with digestion of food and production of B-Vitamins. Prevents fungi growth (candida albicans) helps re-supply good bacteria after antibiotic use. Promotes anti-fungal and anti-viral activity. DDS-1 strain reduces cholesterol levels,

entative, and inhibits
isease causing pathogens.
s rhamnosus - prevention
lls, eradication of harmful
These important lactobacilli
infections and promote the
of vitamin K.
us salivarius - cleanses the
und decayed matter, allows
rgy, protects mucosal
breaks down food in the
intestinal tract allowing vital enzymes
and nutrients to be utilized by the body.
Helps against diarrhea, produces antimicrobial activity.

- *L-Sporogenes / Bacillus coagulans* – a
  transient, versatile microorganism.
  Helps with blood fat levels and fights
  many diseases in the intestine. Take
  during antibiotic treatment. Produces
  enzymes activity, B-vitamin utilization.
  Controls candida albicans, combats
  yeast problems.
- *Streptococcus thermophilus* - transient,
  helps contain tumor development, has
  antibiotic activity. Promotes lactase
  enzyme production, which helps the
  digestion of lactose.
- *Bifidobacterium thermophilum* -
  stimulates lactic acid in the small
  intestine.

- *Bifidobacterium longum* - Helps with nutrient and liquid uptake in the intestinal wall. Inhibit growth of colon, liver and mammary tumors.
- *Streptococcus faecium* - Helps synthesize B-vitamins. A hardy strain of bacteria, which helps production of lactic acid.
- *Lacto bulgaricus* - Helps change pH to an undesirable environment, assists in the breakdown and absorption of proteins. Promotes the production of Lactase enzyme and augments immune system. May help allergic reactions.
- *Streptococcus thermophilus* - stimulates growth, helps production of lactase enzyme. Enhances digestion. Inhibits tumor growth.
- *Bacillus subtilus* - transient microorganism. Reduction of nitrates activates growth of enzymes amylase, protease, and lipase. Stimulates lymphocytes and immune system.
- *Bifidobacteria breve* - Helps in the production of B-vitamins.
- *Bacillus laterosporus* - Immune system enhancer, antibiotic activity. Helpful against Candida Albicans, Crohns disease, parasite infections, the Epstein-Barr virus and more.

- *Lactobaccilus casei* -Helps breakdown bile acids, enzyme production and produces lactic acid. May help allergies.
- *Lactobacillus lactis* - Produces lactic acid, anti-microbials, assists in fat digestion and enzyme production.
- *Streptococcus diacetylacties* - produces anti-microbials and diacetyl acid.
- *Bifidobacterium bifidum* - helps repair cell walls and produces acids, anti-microbials and assists in enzyme production.
- *Lactobacillus plantarum* - Helpful against bacterial infections by not allowing the pathogen to hold on to the intestinal wall.

Q: I am worried about my puppies getting Parvo. We have heard that the parvo vaccination is ineffective in young dogs, what is the truth?

A: The parvo vaccination takes effect after 6 months; a new form of the pharmaceutical may take effect earlier. A natural product called ParvoX is effective against the virus and helps stop dehydration.

Q: Our dogs and cats love canned food, what can we add to the food to make it nutrient rich and healthier?

A: Canned food is flavored water with synthetic vitamins. Supplement canned food usage. Positive Health is in a base of Wild Salmon and Coconut oil with a full complement of active natural plant vitamins, minerals, probiotics and enzymes and more.

Q: Is Coconut Oil beneficial?

A: Yes, please read these articles:

ANTI-CANCER EFFECTS OF COCONUT OIL- LITA LYNN PHD 2001

In 1987 Lim-Sylianco published a 50-year literature review showing the anti-cancer effects of coconut oil. In chemically induced cancers of the colon and breast, coconut oil was by far more protective than unsaturated oils. For example 32% of corn oil eaters got colon cancer whereas only 3% of coconut oil eaters got the cancer. Animals fed unsaturated oils had more tumors. This shows the thyroid-suppressive and hence, immuno-suppressive effect of unsaturated oils. (Cohen et al. 1986).

THYROID-STIMULATING EFFECTS OF COCONUT OIL

Many researchers have reported that coconut oil lowers cholesterol (Blackburn et al 1988, Ahrens and colleagues, 1957). In 1981, Prior et al. showed that islanders with a diet high in coconut oil showed no harmful health effects. When these groups migrated to New Zealand and lowered their daily coconut oil intake, their total cholesterol and especially their LDL cholesterol - the so-called evil one - increased. The cholesterol-lowering properties of coconut oil are a direct result of its ability to stimulate thyroid function. In the presence of adequate thyroid hormone, cholesterol (specifically LDL-cholesterol) is converted by enzymatic processes to the vitally necessary anti-aging steroids, pregnenolone, progesterone and DHEA. These substances are required to help prevent heart disease, obesity, cancer and other diseases associated with chronic degenerative diseases.

MARY G. ENIG, PH.D., F.A.C.N.

Approximately 50% of the fatty acids in coconut fat are lauric acid. Lauric acid is a medium chain fatty acid, which has the additional beneficial function of being formed into monolaurin in the human or animal body. Monolaurin is the antiviral, antibacterial, and antiprotozoal monoglyceride used by the human or animal to destroy lipid-coated viruses such as cytomegalovirus, influenza, various pathogenic bacteria, including listeria monocytogenes and helicobacter pylori, and protozoa such as giardia lamblia. Some studies have also shown some antimicrobial effects of the free lauric acid.

Also, approximately 6-7% of the fatty acids in coconut fat are capric acid. Capric acid is another medium chain fatty acid, which has a similar beneficial function when it is formed into monocaprin in the human or animal body.

A number of fungi, yeast, and protozoa are inactivated or killed by lauric acid or monolaurin. The fungi include several species of ringworm (Isaacs et al 1991). The yeast reported is Candida albicans (Isaacs et al 1991). The protozoan parasite Giardia lamblia is killed by free fatty acids and monoglycerides from hydrolyzed human milk (Hernell et al 1986, Reiner et al 1986, Crouch et al 1991, Isaacs et al 1991). Numerous other protozoa were studied with similar findings; these findings have not yet been published (Jon J. Kabara, private communication, 1997).

CHAPTER THIRTEEN:
RECIPES

BO's LOVE:
   12 oz. desiccated liver
   1 and 1/2 lb barley or rye flour
   8 oz organic oats
   3 organic bouillon cubes
   2 tsp parsley
   1 cup purified water
   2 brown eggs

Put the liver in a processor and blend until fine or a little chunky. Mix flour and oats, then add the crumbled bouillon, eggs and liver. Add water until a firm and sticky dough is made. Spread evenly on 3-4 cookie sheets (1/2" thick), with your cookie cutter, and dip in flour prior to cutting. Bake approximately 25-40 minutes in preheated 350F oven. Refrigerate. Use within 10 days.

SHADOWS SUSHI SURPRISE:
  Organic brown rice
  Boneless organic raw or cooked chicken
    breast
  Seaweed wrap
  Virgin olive oil, coconut oil or wild salmon
    oil
  Flax seed
  Young barley sprouts finely grated

Prepare the rice following the label instructions. Pound the chicken breast with a mallet to make it thin. Cut the chicken into strips. Add a little water to your hands to shape the rice into an oval shape. Put the chicken strips on top of the rice. Add the seaweed wrap to hold everything in place. Brush olive oil lightly over the wrap. Sprinkle top with flax seed and barley sprouts. Refrigerate or freeze portions.

BUDDY'S LOVE BISCUITS

    2 cups barley or rye flour
    1 1/4 cups shredded organic cheese
    1/2 teaspoon garlic powder
    1/4 teaspoon vanilla
    1/8 cup virgin coconut oil
    4 tablespoons purified water

Combine the flour, cheese, garlic, vanilla and oil. Knead well, adding water as needed to stiffen the dough. Roll out on floured wax paper approximately 1/2" thick. Cut with a cookie cutter. Bake in preheated 325F oven for approximately 25-30 minutes on the wire rack. Cookies should be a light golden brown on bottom.

BUBBA'S FANTASY:

2 shredded carrots
2 3/4 cups purified water
1 brown egg ·
1/4 tsp vanilla
2 tsp honey
1 1/2 cups overripe pureed bananas
1/4 cup blueberries
1/4 cup crushed yam
4 cups barley or rye flour
1 tsp baking powder
1 teaspoon cinnamon
1 teaspoon nutmeg
1 teaspoon parsley

Add all wet ingredients in a bowl, add bananas, Mix thoroughly, Set aside. Combine the dry ingredients and mix thoroughly, making sure not to leave any dry mixture on the bottom. Coat the muffin pan, fill pan approximately 1/2" full. Bake in preheated 350F oven approximately 25-35 minutes.

K D GOOD DOG TREATS:

- 2 1/2 cups barley or rye flour
- 1/8 cup coconut oil
- 1/4 cup organic applesauce
  (unsweetened)
- 1/2 cup organic shredded cheese
- 1/4 cup chopped parsley
- 1 brown egg
- 1 teaspoon garlic powder

Combine all ingredients and mix well. Pat the dough on a lightly greased cookie sheet. Score to desired sizes (do not cut all the way through). Bake in preheated 325F oven for approximately 25-35 minutes or until golden brown. Turn off the oven and let cool for a few hours. Break apart and store in the freezer and a sealed jar.

MAXS' BUG OFF FLEAS:
2 cups barley or rye flour
1/2 cup wheat germ
1/2 cup brewers yeast
2-4 cloves garlic (finely minced)
3 tablespoons coconut oil
1 cup organic chicken stock

Combine the flour, wheat germ and brewers yeast. In another bowl, mix the garlic and oil, slowly stirring in the flour mixture alternating with chicken stock. Mix well. Roll out dough 1/2" thick and cut with a cookie cutter. Place on greased cookie sheets. Bake in preheated 400F oven for approximately 30 minutes. Turn off the heat and allow biscuits to dry in the oven for 3-4 hours. Refrigerate or freeze.

TRAVIS' ICE POP:
1 container organic plain yogurt
1-2 mashed overipe bananas
1 teaspoon honey
2 teaspoons peanut butter
1 /8 cup shredded carrots & apples

Mix together, pour contents into an ice cube tray and freeze.

CUDDLES ORGANIC FRUIT CRUNCH:
- 2 3/4 cups spring water
- 1/4 cup organic applesauce
- 1 small jar organic fruit salad (no added sugar)
- 4 cups organic barley or rye flour
- 1 cup cut up organic apple
- 2 teaspoons baking powder
- 1 brown egg
- 1 teaspoon cinnamon
- 4 tablespoons honey

Mix wet ingredients together thoroughly. In a separate bowl, combine dry ingredients. Mix together. Make sure no dry ingredients are left in the bowl. Pour into muffin tins or muffin head tins. Bake in preheated 350F oven for 25-35 minutes. Insert toothpick into center until it comes out dry. Store in container.

FRECKLES VEGETABLE BISCUIT:
   3 cups chopped parsley
   1/4 cup shredded carrots
   1/4 cup shredded zucchini
   1/4 cup organic shredded cheese
   1/8 cup maitake mushroom
   1/8 cup reishi or shitake mushroom
   3 tablespoons coconut oil
   3 cups barley or rye flour
   2 tablespoons wheat or rice bran
   2 teaspoons baking powder
   1/2 to 1 cup spring water

Mix parsley, carrots, zucchini, mushroom, cheese and oil together. Combine all of the dry ingredients in a separate bowl and add to the vegetables. Slowly add 1/2 cup water, mixing well. Dough should be moist. Knead and roll out the dough on a floured piece of wax paper approximately 1/2" thick. Cut with a cookie cutter. Bake at 325F for up to 25-35 minutes or until biscuits have browned. Let cool on wire rack. They will harden as they cool. Store in container.

Chapter Fourteen:
Resources
Supplements

Donsbach
1229 3rd Ave. Suite C
Chula Vista, CA 91911
1-800-359-6547

Doctors Finest Pet Products
711 S. Carson St #4A
Carson City, NV 89701
1-800-470-2001

Crystal Star
4069 Wedgeway Ct.
1-800 736-6015

American Biologics
Chula Vista, CA 91911
1-800-227-4473

Eclectic Institute
14385 SE Lusted Rd
Sandy, OR 97055
1-800-332-4372

Bio-Energetics
1-800-835-0850

Earth's Bounty
9316 Wheatlands Rd
Santee, CA 92071
1-800-736-5609

Mountain Rose Herbs
20818 High St
North San Juan, CA 95960
1-800-879-3337

Great Life Perfomance Pet Products
668 Flinn Ave
Moorpartk, CA 93021
1-805-529-DOGS (3647)

Cheryl's Herbs (Aromatherapy)
836 Hanley Industrial Court
St. Louis, MO 63144
1-314-963-4449

AmeriHerb
PO Box 1968
Ames, IA 50010-1968
Madison, WI 53714
1-800-888-1172

Michaels Thyroid Factors
San Antionio, TX 78244
1-210-661-9257

Ejuva
1-831-457-1323

Boiron
4145 Guardian
Simi Valley, CA
805-527-9883

PHD
PO Box 8313
White Plains, NY 10602
1-800-PHD-1502

Lane Labs
80 Woodland Road
Short Hills, NJ 07078
1-201-467-1108

Grizzly Salmon Oil
1-888-323-5575

FOODS

Halshan
25935 Frampton Ave
Harbor City, CA 90710
1-310-530-7823

Steve's Real Food
1848 Pearl St
Eugene, OR 97401
1-888-526-1900

Pat McKay
1-800-975-7555

Primal
2378 36th Ave
San Francisco, CA 94116
1-866-566-4652

Great Life Dog & Cat Food
668 Flinn Ave
Moorpark, CA 93201
1-805-529-DOGS

Natures Variety
6200 N. 56th St
Lincoln, NE 68504
1-888-519-7387

TREATS

Bow Wow Gourmet Treats
1-877-5- Bow-Wow

Zukes
5800 McLeod Road NE
Albuquerque, NM 87109
1-888-Dog Power

PetsUSA
275 Morgan Ave
Brooklyn, NY 11211
1-866-489-8196

Everyone's Best Friend (Natura)
PO Box 271
Santa Clara, CA 95052
1-800-532-7261

Great Life Barkery
1-805-529-3647

RECOMMENDED READING

Reigning Cats and Dogs, Pat McKay (Oscar Publications)1-800-975-7555

Natural Care Of Pets, Roger DeHaan DVM
1-218-846-9112

Complete Herbal Book for the Dog, Juliette DeBairacli Levy (Arco Publishing)

Food Pets Die For, Ann Martin (New Sage Press)1-503-695-2211

Akita Treasures of Japan (Magnum Publishing-Barbara Bouyet) www.akitabook.com. Excellent book for all dogs

ELLIOTT HARVEY, MH

CHAPTER FIFTEEN:
THE IMPORTANCE OF ENZYMES IN A DIET, BY LINDA ARNDT

INTRODUCTION

During the last 16 years, I have written about the necessity of incorporating enzymes into your dog's diet. To help you better understand the benefits of using enzymes and why they are so important for quality health and longevity, I will try to keep this in lay terms to provide a solid understanding of enzymes. I will address two kinds of enzymes: Digestive Enzymes and Dietary/Metabolic Enzymes.

DIGESTIVE ENZYMES

Digestive enzymes are facilitators, and they have a different job than dietary enzymes in that they are present in all living matter and are necessary for proper digestion. For our pets to obtain proper digestion, they need the digestive enzymes that are normally made by the pancreas and found in the foods we normally eat, provided the food is not cooked. Foods that are heated or processed, for humans or animals, lose 100% of the enzymes. This forces the animal's body to depend entirely on its own pancreatic output of digestive enzymes for digestion of the food.

This is stressful on the system over a long period of time and can cause leukocytosis. There are 4 digestive enzymes: *proteases*, which break down protein; *lipases*, which break down fats or lipids; *amylases*, which break down carbohydrates (principally starch and sugars); and *cellulases*, which break down vegetable matter, including fiber.

The object of "breakdown" is to improve digestion by increasing the availability of nutrients. The faster the breakdown of food, the faster the animal can process it. You can incorporate digestive enzymes into an animal's diet through the use of several products that are compatible with any commercial food or method of feeding.

It is my opinion digestive enzymes in combination with probiotics (friendly yogurt-type bacteria) may well be the key to reducing or eliminating the bloat that often leads to gastric torsion. These two extremely important elements are missing in the vast majority of commercial dog foods. Probiotics and digestive enzymes are critical to keeping a healthy digestive track, and the basis of good health is a healthy gut.

There are only a few commercial food companies that believe digestive enzymes and probiotics are necessary in an animal's diet, and that choose to put these items back in the food after it is processed. This is an important step in the right direction, so when searching for a quality food, make sure the company does so with their products. I use additional digestive and probiotics in the form of daily greens for all my animal's diets, in small amounts, as an added measure of insurance. This is no guarantee, but it is certainly more help than we have had so far in this struggle to control bloat and gastric torsion and other degenerative diseases.

DIETARY/METABOLIC ENZYMES: THE INTERNAL BATTLEGROUND

Before we discuss dietary/metabolic enzymes we must understand the correlation between antioxidant enzymes and free radicals. Free radicals kill molecules in the body, which in turn kill off cells, and the end result of this is disease, decay and, eventually, death. Free radicals are naturally occurring unstable molecules, which damage healthy molecules by stealing electrons. They develop in the body naturally for different reasons including normal metabolism, disease, environmental and physical stress, pollution, pesticides, medicines, injury and radiation, to name a few.

To compensate, our bodies produce antioxidant enzymes to counteract free radicals and cleanse them from our systems through waste products. When we do not provide ourselves with an adequate balanced diet of quality "fresh" foods, it reduces the body's ability to make these chemicals and the reactions necessary for optimum health. In addition to diet, environmental stress and the natural aging process also affects the body's ability to make these critical enzymes.

Nature has designed its food sources to have sufficient enzymes, provided they are not lost in the cooking or processing of foods. However, ingesting foods that are "enzyme-empty" triggers the body's immune system in the opposite manner and the body responds with leukocytosis. This reaction, where white blood cell levels are elevated, occurs after eating cooked or processed foods. By incorporating enzymatic-rich food sources, like sprouted foods, into our diet, we can counteract the cell damage.

If we think of our nutrients such as vitamins, minerals, amino acids, etc., as being the bricks, enzymes are elements necessary to build the walls, the glue that holds it all together. In other words, dietary enzymes are available when we supply the diet with fresh or sprouted foods, which in turn provide the elements necessary for the body to make the chemicals needed to repair free radical damage. I think of dietary enzymes as the mop that goes in and cleans up the spills.

ANTIOXIDANTS

Antioxidants are the body's scavengers; they cleanse the body of any free radical toxins. I think of antioxidants as filters for the body, filters that decrease in our bodies as we age.

Where can we get antioxidants? Antioxidants are found naturally in foods in the form of:

- Antioxidant Vitamins - A, C, E
- Antioxidant Minerals - Selenium, Zinc
- Antioxidant Enzymes - in the form of dietary enzymes found in certain foods, herbs, amino acids, hormones, botanical sources.

AN ILLUSTRATION:

- Your car needs gasoline to run. Gasoline is the energy that powers the car to run.
- Your body needs oxygen to run. Oxygen is the energy that powers a body.

In both cases, this production of energy produces byproducts or toxic waste that needs to be eliminated. Cars do it through exhaust system and the body through its waste system.

Dietary enzyme supplementation is critical for protecting our bodies against damage at a cellular level. Dietary enzymes provide anti-aging properties that minimize the ravages of time on our bodies. In humans, damage is seen as wrinkles, liver spots, arthritis, and other degenerative diseases caused when free radicals kill off molecules in the body.

The benefits of dietary enzyme supplementation include:

- reducing the effects of aging, wrinkles, liver spots etc.
- aiding in disease prevention
- aiding in the prevention of cancer and debilitating diseases
- minimizing the negative effects of cancer therapies
- reducing the size of cancerous tumors
- boosting the immune system
- reducing inflammation /soreness of muscle and joint pain
- retarding periodontal disease
- retarding the progression of disease processes
- preventing heart disease
- speeding healing after surgery
- preventing reperfusion after bloat/ torsion surgery
- reducing the negative effects of inoculations

- reducing the negative effects of anesthetics
- aiding in reproduction problems, regulating cycles, infertility and sterility
- cleansing the system of allergic reactions

REPRODUCTION

I know several breeders that have managed to regulate their bitches' seasons, plus get their males' poor sperm count and motility back on track through the use of dietary enzymes supplements.

HEALING AND VACCINES

I think dietary enzymes are a must for animals going through major surgery, particularly after torsion surgery. In addition, we notice that when our puppies are taking enzymes prior to cropping, they tend to come out of anesthesia quicker and heal faster. During vaccinations the enzymes help eliminate toxins from the body and have been very effective in countering the effects of vaccinosis.

OPTIONS

Once again, if our pets regularly ate a more natural whole food diet, they would be getting these important components everyday. But for many people, preparing a raw food diet for their animals is cumbersome, difficult, and problematic. Because few have the time or the knowledge to put together the properly balanced diet that incorporates all the components necessary to maintain a pet's metabolism, I have found other options.

If you are willing to take the time to prepare a raw food diet, you have to educate yourself on the nutritional needs of your pet and dedicate the time it takes to prepare a truly varied diet so there are no nutritional deficiencies or imbalances.

For most of us, this is impossible. I have seen too many cases where people start this type of totally raw diet and fall into a routine where they stop varying the diet. Suddenly, their animals start showing signs of nutritional deficiencies, at which time I get a call asking, "What do I do to correct this problem?"

Therefore, it is my opinion that, for the majority of pet owners, the simplest, most comprehensive way to feed their animals is to use a high-quality kibble and whole

188

food supplements such as dietary enzymes, probiotics and digestive enzymes.

I hope this article clarifies the difference between dietary enzymes and digestive enzymes.

INDEX

Y

Z

Elliott Harvey, MH

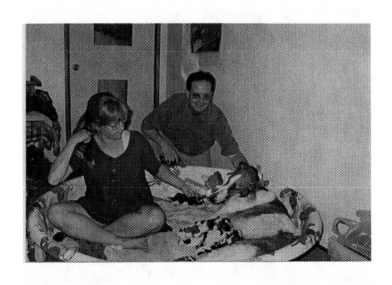

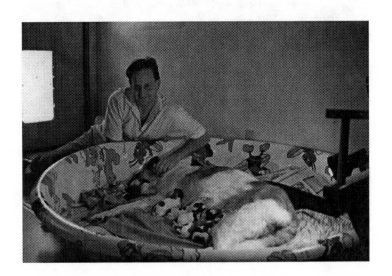

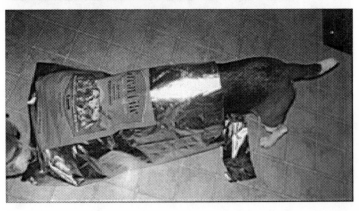

Printed in the United States
113321LV00006B/186/A